The Victorian
Steam Locomotive

William Stroudley 2-2-2 tender Passenger Locomotive, Grosvenor, constructed for the LBSCR.

The Victorian Steam Locomotive

Its Design and Development 1804–1897

G.D. Dempsey, C.E.
&
D. Kinnear Clark, C.E.

PEN & SWORD TRANSPORT

First published in Great Britain in 2015
and republished in this format in 2022 by
Pen & Sword Transport
an imprint of
Pen & Sword Books Ltd
Yorkshire – Philadelphia

ISBN 978 1 39907 709 5

Typeset in Ehrhardt by Mac Style Ltd
Printed on FSC accredited paper by 4edge Ltd, Essex, SS5 4AD

Pen & Sword Books Limited incorporates the imprints of Atlas,
Archaeology, Aviation, Discovery, Family History, Fiction,
History, Maritime, Military, Military Classics, Politics, Select,
Transport, True Crime, Air World, Frontline Publishing, Leo
Cooper, Remember When, Seaforth Publishing, The Praetorian
Press, Wharncliffe Local History, Wharncliffe Transport,
Wharncliffe True Crime, White Owl and After the Battle.

For a complete list of Pen & Sword titles please contact

PEN & SWORD BOOKS LIMITED
47 Church Street, Barnsley, South Yorkshire, S70 2AS, England
E-mail: enquiries@pen-and-sword.co.uk
Website: www.pen-and-sword.co.uk
or
PEN AND SWORD BOOKS
1950 Lawrence Rd, Havertown, PA 19083, USA
E-mail: Uspen-and-sword@casematepublishers.com
Website: www.penandswordbooks.com

Contents

Foreword

For most of us who try to keep the steam age alive we can become blasé about its history, but like everything in life things develop in their own way. However, when man's creative hand is involved then the results are amazing. From 1804 to 1897 the world changed beyond anyone's comprehension. It took 139 years to get from the first telephone to the mobiles we all take for granted today, but they're still telephones! This book shows how we moved from a simple idea of boiling water to make steam to generate power, to the steam engine we still know and love. There have been lots of inventors who try to improve on our Victorian Heritage but they are just tweaks. This book plots the development of the Steam Locomotive and is a book I recommend to all who love them or wish to work on their preservation. A fascinating read.

Dr Pete Waterman
OBE, DL. President of the Combustion Engineering
Association. Fellow of the Institute of Cast Metal Engineers

Preface

The Locomotive Engine is a microcosm of engineering, which never fails to command the admiration of technical men, and the wonder of everybody. As Mr Dempsey truly remarks, 'A locomotive engine followed by a train of carriages always impresses the spectator as a remarkable exhibition of inanimate power.'

In the first part of this elementary treatise, descriptive of the locomotive engine, whilst I have adhered to the outlines of Mr Dempsey's original description, I have considerably abridged it, although preserving, nearly in its entirety, the illustrated account of the standard six-wheeled passenger locomotive, constructed by Messrs. Robert Stephenson and Co, in the era of 1838–43.

The second part of this volume is descriptive of the modern locomotive, in which the distinguishing types of English engines are exhibited by examples; and one of them, an express passenger locomotive, constructed by Messrs. Beyer, Peacock, and Co, is fully described and illustrated in detail.

The contrast thus afforded between the early locomotive and the perfected engine of today, supplies, it is believed, an instructive study for the student, and material for reflection to the more advanced engineer.

In the account of the modern locomotive, the general principles which regulate the design and construction of the framing, the boiler, and the engine proper, are enunciated and explained; and the practice of coal burning in locomotives is treated, historically and practically, with expositions of the best practice of the present day.

A section on the resistance of engines and trains on railways is added, in which the chief contingencies affecting the resistance of trains and the performance of engines, are brought into consideration.

D. K. Clark

Part I

Historical Sketch and Description of the Locomotive Engine

A locomotive engine, followed by a train of carriages, always impresses the spectator as a remarkable exhibition of inanimate power. The once familiar, but now ancient, spectacle of the mail-coach, whirled along by its glowing team, was wont to excite admiration by its evidence of equestrian training and discipline; but the means of its movement were palpable, and reflection was scarcely prompted by the sight. Of two witnesses – one from the workshop, the other from the stable – the latter could probably the best appreciate the principles of the draught, and explain why the leaders and the wheelers were selected for their respective places; but the sight of a complicated and apparently cumbrous machine, moving itself under the mere direction of a human driver, forcibly overcoming not only its own inertia, but that of the many heavy carriages and trucks which helplessly follow in its chains, is a demonstration of mechanical agency which, however often it may be witnessed, arrests the attention in every instance, and leads the mind to contemplate the means employed, or to inquire what those means are.

Let us become such inquirers, and endeavour to ascertain those means. We have just seen a friend 'off by railway'; and, having had to wait some time on the platform of the station, glanced at the hissing leader of the train, which by brazen plate proclaimed itself to be a 'Hurricane', 'Thunderer', 'Meteor', or other symbol of speed and power. While stationary, we noticed the engine had six wheels – perhaps all of one size – and having a long horizontal bar of metal outside the wheels attached to the spokes of the three wheels on either side, the wheels being thus connected or coupled together. Beneath the engine, a bright fire-light gleamed near the hinder end; while, in front, puffs of steam were issuing and hissing with deafening noise. A variety of bars, rods, and other pieces of shining metal appeared to be fixed under the body of the machine; but the arrangement was too complicated to allow us to trace the connection between these and the wheels; and the belief in their utility was chiefly induced by seeing the engine-driver descend from his standing-place at the back of the engine, and caressingly wipe them with a handful of greasy rags. We noticed, however, that the whole machine appeared externally to consist of three portions, of different shapes and sizes. The front part, on the centre of which the chimney or funnel was placed, was curved on the top, had straight sides and bottom, and was larger than the long middle or cylindrical portion of the engine; while the back portion was again of increased width, and seemed to descend nearer the ground than the front. A door in this part of the apparatus was opened by the driver's assistant, or stoker, who flung in two or three shovels of coals from the tender; and we were thus prepared to understand the explanation of a bystander, that this hind part of the engine is called the *fire-box*. The central cylindrical part was also described to be the *boiler*, and the front portion the *smoke-box*.

But the second bell rings; the passengers are all seated, and the carriage-doors closed; the last shaking of hands has been hurried through an open window; the porters scour along the side of the train, and warn the friends on the platform to stand back; the driver jumps into his place, and – while the stoker releases the break from the wheels of the tender – turns a small handle and sounds the whistle, and by the movement of other handles starts the engine. The puffs of steam from below cease, and the hissing is succeeded by a sound as of a giant panting for breath. Presently his metal lungs seem forced into action, and the laboured sound gradually quickens into a rapid throb that dies away in the distance, like the pulsations of Hercules borne on the wings of the wind.

From the platform, let us turn to study the internal mechanism of the engine.

We all know, to begin with, that the machine is impelled by steam, which it produces within itself, being fed at intervals with the two ingredients of fuel and water from the tender. The former we have seen supplied by the stoker with a shovel; the latter is administered directly from the tender through a pipe, which is aptly termed the *feed-pipe*. We all know also, that when water is so heated as to become steam, it expands in bulk and thus produces motion, which the *engine* converts to a useful purpose. In this elementary view, we are aware that all steam-engines resemble each other, whether in the ponderous forms of *marine engines*, working paddles or giving revolutions to screws; of *stationary engines*, pumping up water for supplying towns and cities, or actuating the elaborate mechanism of manufactures; or of *locomotive engines*, drawing trains of enormous weight on iron roads at velocities which, in the times of mere animal agency, would have been deemed chimerical if not fabulous.

Portable machinery, however, always involves considerations which do not arise in the designing of stationary apparatus. Thus locomotive engines are limited in external dimensions and in gross weight; while for fixed engines the size and the weight are points rarely taken into account. In locomotives, moreover, it is necessary to provide the most extended space for the operation of heat for the production of power; and thus, while a large boiler and a single internal tube are admissible, and sufficient for generating steam for a stationary engine, a small boiler is imperative in a locomotive, and the required heated surface for the rapid creation of steam is obtained by introducing within the boiler a large number of small tubes. In short, the great desideratum in designing a locomotive engine is to obtain the greatest possible amount of power with the smallest possible size of the machine.

The most essential parts in all steam-engines are the cylinder and the piston. We all know that the cylinder corresponds with the barrel of a pump, and that the piston is similar to the disc inside the pump, which the pump-maker calls the sucker. The common form of syringe, known by schoolboys as a *squirt,* is another instance of cylinder and piston familiar to all of us. We can readily understand how the expansion or swelling of the boiling water, as it becomes steam and is admitted within one end of a cylinder, will force the piston to the other end of it. We can also understand that if the steam be then let out of the cylinder, and fresh steam be admitted at the other end, behind the piston, the piston will be driven back again to the end from which it first started, and that these successive operations may be repeated, and the piston thus made to travel alternately from one to the other end of the cylinder.

We shall thus have produced what mechanics call a *reciprocating rectilineal* motion; that is, the piston will be moved backwards and forwards in a straight line.

The next purpose to be accomplished is to make use of this motion for turning wheels round. Our piston is supposed to be provided with a piston-rod, which again corresponds with the rod of the pump and the handle of the syringe. This rod or handle is made long enough to project beyond the end of the cylinder at all times, for the purpose of connecting it with the next important part of the apparatus, viz. the *crank.* The wheels to be turned round are fixed on an axle; and this axle has a bend in it so formed, that while the two ends of the axle are in one straight line the bent portion is some inches out of that straight line. 'With the addition of a rod for connecting the piston-rod with the crank, and which is hence called the *connecting-rod,* our elementary apparatus will be completed, and we may now make a little sketch to assure ourselves that we understand it.

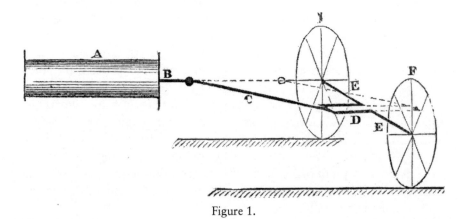

Figure 1.

In this figure A is the cylinder with the piston within it, B the piston-rod, C the connecting-rod, D the crank on the axle E E of the wheels F F. The dotted lines show the position of the parts when the piston has reached the other end of the cylinder. The foot-lathe used by the turner, and the apparatus of the itinerant knife-grinder, are familiar examples of cranks for giving rotatory motion to wheels by the alternate movement of the treadles. Now, if we imagine a tea-kettle, saucepan, or any other closed vessel in which water may be boiled, to be so connected with the cylinder in our sketch that the steam shall enter alternately at each end of the cylinder, the steam being discharged at every *stroke* of the piston, or as soon as it has driven the piston from one end to the other, we shall have the motive mechanism of a locomotive steam-engine. All the additions to be made to it, to convert it into the most complicated production of engineering art, consist of apparatus for boiling the water, for regulating the admission of steam into the cylinder, and the discharge of it from the cylinder, for providing adequate draught for the fire, and for giving to the driver of the engine the means of starting and stopping the movement of the engine, and of reversing the direction of its movement on the instant, as occasion may require.

A sketch of the history of the locomotive engine will show us the earliest forms in which it was designed, and the several improvements and additions made upon them; and by thus watching the growth of the machine, step by step as it were, we shall readily trace the gradual progress from rude simplicity to the studied complication of parts which bewilder the eyes and the understanding of the uninitiated spectator of a modern locomotive.

The name which the world has learned to associate with the steam-engine as a stationary machine, must also be quoted in reference to its birth as an apparatus for locomotion. James Watt has recorded: – 'My attention was first directed in 1759 to the subject of steam-engines by Dr Robison, then a student in the University of Glasgow, and nearly of my own age. Robison at that time threw out the idea of applying the power of the steam-engine to the moving of wheel-carriages, and to other purposes; but the scheme was not matured, and was soon abandoned on his going abroad.'

This appears to be the earliest recorded notion of the locomotive steam-engine, which Watt seems to have worked out into a practical form that he included in a patent obtained in the year 1784.

Watt's locomotive, as described in the specification of his patent, was to have a boiler formed of staves of wood bound with hoops of iron. An iron furnace was to be fixed within this boiler in such a manner that it should be nearly surrounded by water. The boiler and cylinder were to be fixed on a carriage having wheels worked by a piston moving a length or stroke of 12 inches within the cylinder, 7 inches in diameter. The same purpose, now usually effected with the *crank,* was, in Watt's locomotive, to be accomplished by *sun-and-planet wheels,* that is, by two cogged or toothed wheels, one of which would be fixed on the same axle as the wheels supporting the carriage, and the other made to revolve round it by the engagement of their teeth or cogs. The centre of the revolving wheel being connected with one end of the connecting-rod, and the piston-rod with the other end of it, the reciprocating motion of the piston would produce a rotatory motion of the carriage-wheels. Watt, however, having become actively and profitably engaged in his improvements of stationary engines, did not prosecute the locomotive scheme; and William Murdoch appears to have been the earliest constructor of a locomotive steam-engine. The date of this apparatus is recorded as 1784, the same year in which Watt's patent was obtained. Murdoch's locomotive, which can be regarded only as a toy, had a copper boiler with an oblique flue within it, and was heated by a spirit lamp. The piston had a stroke of 2 inches and was ¾ inch in diameter. The cylinder was fixed upright on the top of the boiler, and a connecting-rod and crank, &c, were employed for giving motion to the axle of the driving-wheel, or the *driving-axle* (as it is called). The carriage is described to have been supported on three wheels, and the size of these wheels will convey a notion of the dimensions of the entire apparatus. The two wheels on the driving-axle were 9¾ inches, and the third or leading wheel 4¾ inches, in diameter. This miniature engine was, however, provided with valves for regulating the passage of the steam, and is recorded to have beaten its inventor on one occasion when he wished to test its speed.

Eighteen years elapsed before any useful result was recognised as attainable by the application of steam to locomotive machinery. Murdoch's defeat by his three-wheeled toy might have suggested a practical purpose, in producing an enlarged and improved edition of it, but it does not appear to have done so; and to Richard Trevithick belongs the merit of having constructed the first experimental locomotive steam-engine, and demonstrated its value as an instrument of draught. A patent was obtained, 24 March 1802, by Richard Trevithick and Andrew Vivian, of Cornwall, for 'methods of improving the construction of steam-engines, and their application for driving carriages and other purposes'. The experimental engine which was made according to this patent, and exhibited to the public in traversing the roadway near Euston Square, London, had four wheels – viz. two small front wheels for guiding, and two large hind wheels – which received motion from the steam. In accordance with his improvements in stationary engines, included in the same patent, Trevithick in his locomotive abandoned the idea of *condensing* the steam (which had been the great purpose of 'Watt's inventions), and adopted the *high-pressure* principle. The engine had one cylinder, placed horizontally and enclosed with the boiler and furnace in a casing placed behind the axle of the driving-wheels. The piston-rod was connected – not with the axle of the wheels, but with a separate axle, on which the crank was formed. The *crank-axle* was thus distinguished from the *driving-axle,* and the motion was imparted from the former to the latter by means of two toothed wheels of equal size – one on each of the axles, and which wheels were fitted or *geared to* work together. The *steam-cocks* for regulating the passage of the steam to and from the cylinder were opened and shut by being connected with the *crank-axle.* A force-pump, for injecting hot water into the boiler, from the casing surrounding the cylinder, &c, was also worked with a rod attached to the crank-axle. In order to maintain the fire with sufficient activity for producing the required quantity of steam, bellows were provided, and were, like the cocks and pump, worked from the crank-axle.

In 1804, Trevithick placed another locomotive engine on a tram-road at Merthyr Tydvil, in South Wales, which engine differed in some respects from the experimental one just described. In the later engine, the cylinder was placed upright, or vertically, and the boiler was of cylindrical form with flat ends. A double or bent flue passed through the boiler, and the furnace and the greater part of the cylinder were also within it. The cylinder of this engine was 8 inches in diameter, and had a stroke of 4 feet 6 inches. It drew a load of 10 tons of bar iron, besides the trucks holding it, at the rate of 5 miles per hour, for a distance of 9 miles, consuming only the water contained in the boiler at starting. In this engine, the used steam was ejected into the chimney, thus promoting the draught and dispensing with the bellows provided in the first engine of the same inventor.

Trevithick's locomotive of 1804 does not appear to have been followed by any considerable improvement or alteration until the year 1811, when a patent was obtained, dated 10 April, by Mr John Blenkinsop, for 'certain mechanical means' of conveying coals, &c, which included the suggestion of a toothed wheel attached to the engine, to work in a rack to be fixed along one side of the rails of the road. This invention or adaptation was intended to obviate the inconvenience that had occasionally arisen from the *slipping round* of the wheels on the tramways without advancing the engine. This want of adhesion, or *bite,* of the wheels on the trams or rails, was afterwards found to be remediable by an improved distribution of the weight on the wheels, which has rendered unnecessary the rack proposed by Blenkinsop, the chain by the Chapmans, and the automatic legs by Brunton, all of which expedients were devised to overcome the same supposed difficulty.

Blenkinsop's locomotive, however, is further noticeable as having first employed *two cylinders,* which worked alternately from the *axle* or *shaft.*

In the year 1814, a locomotive engine was constructed at the Killingworth Colliery by the celebrated George Stephenson. This engine had two cylinders placed vertically, partly within and partly above the boiler, which was cylindrical, 8 feet long, and 2 feet 10 inches in diameter, with an internal flue 1 foot 8 inches in diameter. The cylinder was 8 inches in diameter, and the piston had a stroke of 2 feet. The connecting-rods had cranks, each of which had a spur-wheel fixed on its axle, and these spur-wheels gave motion to two other spur-wheels, one on either side, fixed on the axles of the carriage-wheels. Between the spur-wheels on the cranks of the connecting-rods, a central spur-wheel was provided, which was useful in preserving the cranks at right angles to each other, and in governing the effect of the propelling power. The spur-wheels on the axles of the carriage-wheels were 2 feet in diameter, and the three other spur-wheels were each 1 foot in diameter, the arrangement being as here sketched.

In this figure, A A represent the two connecting-rods from the piston-rods, and B B the cranks on the axles of the spur-wheels, C C; D is the central spur-wheel, and E E are the spur-wheels on the axles of the carriage-wheels, F F. This engine is reported to have drawn 30 tons at the rate of 4 miles an hour, but the spur-wheels were found to wear rapidly, and to make a great noise; and in the following year, Mr Stephenson introduced an improvement which superseded the necessity for the spur gear altogether. This improvement was patented on the 28 February 1815, by Mr Stephenson in conjunction with Mr Dodd, and the improvement is described to have consisted in 'the application of a pin upon one of the

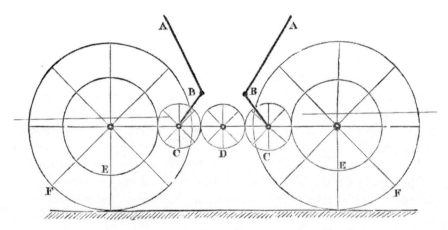

Figure 2.

spokes of the wheels that supported the engine by which it travelled upon the railroad, the lower end of the connecting-rod being attached to it by what is termed a ball-and-socket joint; the other end of the connecting-rod being attached to the cross beam, worked up and down by the piston'. The patentees proposed two methods of keeping the cranks at right angles to each other; viz. to crank the axle on which each pair of wheels was fixed, and provide a connecting-rod between them, or to use an endless chain, of which the links should work into teeth of wheels fixed on the axles of the carriage-wheels. In the engines constructed under this patent, either at the period of this date or subsequently, Mr Stephenson discharged the used *steam, into the chimney* for the purpose of aiding the draught of air through the furnace, and, consequently, the rapid production of steam. The immediate effect of this improvement is reported to have been the *doubling* of the speed of the engine.

On the 30 September 1816, Mr Stephenson, conjointly with Mr Losh, obtained a patent for further improvements, which consisted 'in sustaining the weight, or a proportion of the weight, of the engine upon pistons, movable in the cylinders, into which the steam or water of the boiler is allowed to enter, in order to press upon such pistons; and which pistons are, by the intervention of certain levers and connecting-rods, or by any other effective contrivance, made to bear upon the axles of the wheels of the carriage upon which the engine rests. When, therefore, the steam presses upon the piston, the weight is transmitted to the axle by the piston-rod, and the reaction of that pressure takes as much weight off the engine. If, therefore, the cylinders are of sufficient area, so that the pressure of the steam upon the whole of the pistons is equal to the weight of the engine, the engine will be lifted up, as it were, or entirely supported by the steam, which thus forms a kind of spring of the nicest elasticity.' The furnace was within the boiler of these engines, the endless chain was employed, and six wheels were used instead of four.

During the thirteen years which elapsed between 1816 and 1829, many minor improvements were introduced in locomotive mechanism. Mr Stephenson substituted *coupling-rods outside the wheels,* and connected to their spokes, for the endless chains he had previously used in the Killingworth engines; steel springs were introduced between the engine-frame and the axle-boxes; and tires of wrought iron were applied to the driving-wheels.

It is recorded, that in the year 1825 locomotives were constructed upon eight wheels, arranged in two sets of four each, each set being attached to a separate frame, or *bogie.* Each of these frames was connected with the frame of the engine by means of a swivel joint, and thus great freedom was obtained for passing round sharp curves in the road, rail, or tramway. The proposition for these bogie-frames had been made in a patent obtained by Messrs. Chapman in the year 1812.

Mr Stephenson's 'Killingworth Engine', as it was used previous to the year 1829, had four wheels, 4 feet in diameter and coupled. The boiler, of wrought iron, was cylindrical, 4 feet in diameter and 9 feet long, with slightly convex ends. A fire tube, 1 foot 10 inches in diameter, was fixed within the boiler, the fire-grate being placed in one end of the tube, while the other end led into the chimney. Two cylinders were provided, sunk upright in the boiler, one at each end of it, and each cylinder, by means of piston-rod, connecting-rods, &c, worked one of the pairs of wheels. The performance of this engine, which weighed 6½ tons – or with tender, fuel, and water, 10 tons – was reported to equal 50 tons *gross* load – that is, including carriages or waggons, engine, and tender – at the rate of 6 miles per hour on a level, 15 cubic feet of water being evaporated per hour.

But the great desideratum for attaining *velocity* was yet wanting. 'Within the necessarily limited space for the locomotive boiler, means were yet required for boiling the water *fast enough* to produce the quantity of steam indispensable for rapidity of motion. The method for obtaining this object, which has since been so successfully adopted, was proposed by a French engineer, M. Seguin, in a patent in February 1828. This method consisted in increasing the heating surface within the boiler, without increasing its external dimensions, by inserting a great number of small tubes, through which the heated air circulated in streams, the water being contained in the boiler, and thus surrounding the tubes. The *evaporative power* of the apparatus was thus vastly augmented. This *multitubular flue boiler* (afterwards introduced in this country by Mr H. Booth), added to the *steam-jet in the chimney* for promoting draught, completed the means of locomotive velocity, and these were the two distinguishing features of the successful 'Rocket,' the discharge of which in the year 1829 established the locomotive steam-engine as the champion over all competing agents of conveyance, and cleared the air of the thick clouds of prejudice by which the merits of the infant railway system were at that period obscured.

The railway between Liverpool and Manchester was, at the time referred to, nearly completed; and the directors, anxious, of course, to obtain the most economical power for working their railway, were yet uncertain as to the instruments to be applied for securing that object. Horses had been suggested, and, as an improvement, stationary steam-engines were proposed, which should draw the carriages with ropes or chains; but the results which had already been effected with locomotive engines induced the directors of the company to invite a competition for supplying the best form of such engine, and to offer a reward for the one which might the most successfully comply with certain conditions.

These conditions, as laid down by the directors on the 25 April 1829, were as follows:

1. The engine should consume its own smoke.
2. An engine of 6 tons weight should draw 20 tons at 10 miles an hour, with a pressure of not more than 50 pounds per square inch.
3. Two safety-valves to be provided, one beyond the reach of the engine-driver.
4. The engine to have springs, and six wheels, and to be not more than 15 feet high to the top of the chimney.
5. The total weight of 6 tons to include water; but a less weight to be preferred, if drawing a proportionate weight; and an engine weighing only 4½ tons might be put on four wheels.
6. A mercurial gauge, to show the pressure above 45lbs to the inch, and to blow out at the pressure of 60lbs.
7. The engine to be delivered in Liverpool, not later than 1 October 1829; and,
8. The price of the engine to be not more than £500.

The time for delivery was afterwards extended to the 6 October. The trial way was chosen at Rainhill, 9 miles from Liverpool, on a level portion of the railway, 2 miles in length. Five engines were named for the trial, but three only competed – viz. the 'Novelty', by Messrs. Braithwaite and Ericson; the 'Sanspareil', by Mr Hackworth; and the 'Rocket', by Messrs. George and Robert Stephenson. The first two were disabled by accidents during the trial, and the 'Rocket' was the only one that fulfilled the conditions, and was accordingly adjudged deserving of the £500 reward offered by the directors.

The 'Rocket' was mounted on four wheels, not coupled or connected together. The boiler was cylindrical, 6 feet long, and 3 feet 4 inches in diameter, and contained *twenty-five copper tubes,* 3 inches in diameter, through which the *heated air* from the furnace passed on its way towards the chimney. The furnace, situated at the rear end of the engine, was 2 feet wide and 3 feet high, and had an external casing, between which and the fire-box a space of 3 inches was provided, and filled with water, communicating with the boiler. The two cylinders, placed one on each side of the boiler in an oblique position, were 8 inches in diameter, and the pistons had strokes of 16½ inches. The connecting-rods from the piston-rods worked the front pair of wheels, which were about 4 feet 8 inches in diameter. The used steam was discharged into the chimney.

The surface of the fire-grate was equal to 6 superficial feet; that of the fire-box was 20 feet; and the total surface of the tubes exposed to the heated air was equal to 117¾ superficial feet. The weight of the 'Rocket', including water in boiler, was 4 tons 5cwt. The load consisted of a loaded tender, weighing 3 tons 4cwt and 2lbs, and of two loaded carriages, weighing together 9 tons 10cwt 3qrs and 26lbs, and making a total *drawn* weight of 12 tons 15cwt, or a total weight of *train* equal to 17 tons. This engine attained the speed of 35 miles per hour without a load, and of 24 miles per hour drawing three times its own weight. Its average speed was reported at $13^8/_{10}$ miles per hour; consumption of coke per mile, for each ton of total weight of train, $^{91}/_{100}$lb, or $11^7/_{10}$lbs for each cubic foot of water evaporated or turned into steam.

A comparison of the 'Rocket' with the 'Killingworth' engine shows that the former moved 40 tons at $13^1/_3$ miles per hour, whilst the latter moved the same weight at only 6 miles per hour.

Following the 'Rocket,' Mr Stephenson constructed seven or eight other engines for the Liverpool and Manchester Railway, and in each of these engines the heating flue-surface was gradually extended from that of 25 tubes 3 inches in diameter (in the 'Rocket'), to 90 tubes of 2 inches in diameter; while the cylinders were increased from 8 to 11 inches in diameter.

While Mr Stephenson was thus improving the locomotive engine and augmenting its power, other engineers were also busy in parallel courses of advancement; but most of the essential features of the 'Rocket' were retained, and improvements were directed to modifications of detail, rather than to any alteration of its principal arrangements, or any addition to their number.

In the 'Planet', however, the ninth engine built by Mr Stephenson for the Liverpool and Manchester Railway, a happy combination was effected of all former good qualities, and the result was an engine which displayed several improvements.

As this engine so far excelled all its predecessors that it became the acknowledged model for succeeding engines, a brief description of it is necessary in this place:

The 'Planet' was carried on four wheels – viz. two leading-wheels 3 feet in diameter, and two driving-wheels 5 feet in diameter. The boiler was 6 feet 6 inches long and 3 feet in diameter, containing 129 tubes, each $1^5/_8$ inch in diameter. The heating surface of the fire-box was equal to 37¼ superficial feet, and that of the tubes 370 feet. The cylinders were 11 inches in diameter, and the pistons had a stroke of 16 inches. The weight of the engine, when empty, was 8 tons; or, with coke and water, 9 tons. The weight of the tender, including its load of coke and water, was 4 tons; or a total weight of engine and tender, charged, of 13 tons. The cylinders were horizontal, placed *inside the smoke-box,* and two cranks were provided on the driving-axle for receiving the power. On 4 December 1830, the 'Planet', on its first trial, took a train of 76 tons of passengers and goods from Liverpool to Manchester in 2 hours and 39 minutes; its greatest velocity, on a level, being at the rate of 15½ miles per hour.

The annexed Fig. 3 shows, in outline, the general arrangement of the 'Planet' engine, in which, it may be noted, the smaller or leading wheels were only 5 feet in advance of the driving-wheels; and that, whilst the cylinder and the smoke-box considerably overhung the leading-wheels in front, the fire-box also considerably overhung the driving-wheels behind, making a total length of 15 feet.

The success of the arrangements combined in the 'Planet' formed a new point of departure for the improvement and development of the locomotive. New locomotives were constructed for the Liverpool and Manchester Railway, on the model of the inside-cylinder engine, and the pattern was early imitated for other railways. But the increased weight and speed of the locomotives of the 'Planet' class gave rise to a new difficulty. They, by their comparatively great weight, short-wheel base, and overhung masses, disorganised the way over which they ran. It was imperative that immediate measures should be taken; and whilst it was resolved to substitute rails of greater strength for the existing rails, it was determined to add a pair of wheels to the engine behind the fire-box,

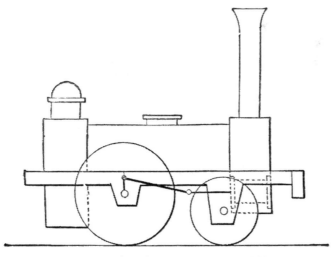

Figure 3. The 'Planet' Locomotive, 1830.

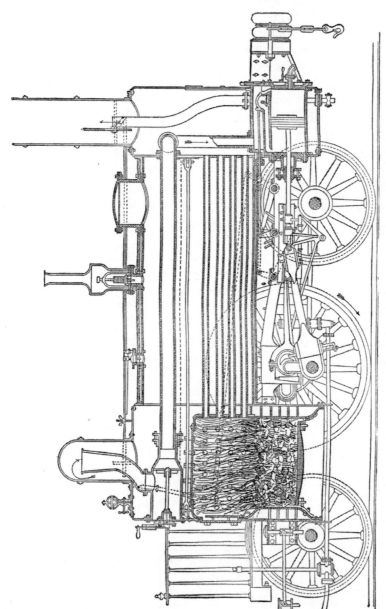

Figure 4. Robert Stephenson's six-wheeled Locomotive, 1838. Longitudinal Section.

constituting it a six-wheel engine, and extending the base to 9 feet; whilst new engines were constructed on the same arrangement as exhibited in Fig. 4, showing the locomotive engine – thus matured as a six-wheeled engine – as it was constructed by Messrs. Robert Stephenson and Co, about the year 1838. The cylinders were 12 inches in diameter, the pistons had a stroke of 18 inches, and the driving-wheels were 5 feet in diameter. The wheel-base, or distance apart, of the extreme axles, was 10 feet. The working pressure of steam in the boiler was 50lbs per square inch. The weight of the engine, empty, was 10 tons; and, holding water and fuel, in working order, it amounted to 12 tons, which was distributed on the three pairs of wheels as follows:

Leading-wheels	4 tons
Driving-wheels	6 tons
Trailing-wheels	<u>2 tons</u>
	12 tons

[In order to mark the progress of construction, the following description of this locomotive is retained, in abstract, from the description given by Mr Dempsey – a reproduction of Mr W. P. Marshall's excellent account of the Stephenson six-wheeled locomotive of the era of 1838. – D. K. C]

The Boiler
Taking the boiler first, it consists of several distinct parts: the cylindrical portion, called peculiarly the boiler; the external fire-box, communicating with it; the internal fire-box, containing the fire-grate; and the tubes, communicating between the internal firebox and the smoke-box, upon which the chimney is fixed.

The boiler is a cylinder 7 feet 6 inches long, and 3 feet 6 inches in diameter outside; it is made of wrought-iron plates $5/_{16}$ inch thick, lapping over each other, and joined together by iron rivets $7/_8$ of an inch in diameter and $1^3/_4$ inch apart. The rivets, inserted red-hot, contract in cooling, drawing the plates forcibly together, and making a very close joint.

The boiler is covered with wood 1 inch thick, in the form of longitudinal staves, bound round by iron hoops, screwed together at the bottom. This casing of wood is for the purpose of retaining the heat, and preventing the heat from being carried off through the air when the engine is moving rapidly, wood being an imperfect conductor of heat.

Fire-boxes

The External Fire-box, or fire-box shell, is a box nearly square, 4 feet wide outside, and 3 feet 7½ inches long in the direction of the boiler, made of wrought-iron plates ⁵/₁₆ inch thick, like those of the boiler; the bottom is 2 feet 1 inch below the boiler, and the upper part is a semi-cylinder, concentric with the boiler. The fire-box is open at the bottom, and has a circular opening cut in the front side, of the same size as the boiler, and corresponding to it; the boiler being fastened to it by means of angle-iron, as shown in the section, Fig. 5. The angle-iron A is bent round the boiler at the place of its junction with the fire-box, and riveted to the plates B and C of the boiler and fire-box. The plates composing the front and back of the fire-box are bent inwards at right angles all round, forming flanches upon which the plates of the sides and top are riveted.

The Internal Fire-box is similar to the external, but flat at the top, and closed at all sides except the bottom; a clear space of 3½ inches is left all round between it and the external fire-box, and at the side next to the boiler the space is 4 inches. The internal fire-box is made of copper plates ⁷/₁₆ inch thick, except the side next the boiler, which is ⁷/₈ inch thick; but all of the plate, except the circular portion opposite to the boiler, is beaten down until it is only ⁷/₁₆ inch thick, the same as the rest. The roof and sides of the box are formed of one plate, and another plate forms

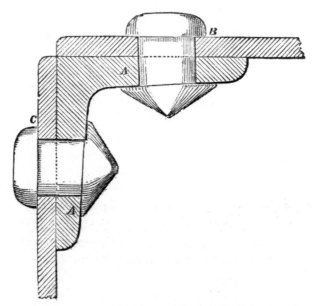

Figure 5. Section at junction of boiler and fire-box shell, lower side. ½ size.

the back, corresponding to that in the front next the boiler: the front and back plates are turned inwards at the edges, like those of the external fire-box, and the other plate fixed to them by ¾ inch copper rivets. The internal fire-box is fastened at the bottom to the external by setting the plates out until they touch the outer plates, and riveting them together with copper rivets. An oval hole, 14 inches wide and 12 inches high, is cut in the back plate of both fire-boxes for the fire-door; the plate of the internal fire-box is set. out all round it to meet the outer plate, and the two are fixed together by a row of copper rivets. The fire-door consists of two wrought-iron plates connected together by rivets, leaving a space of ½ inch between them: this protects the outer plate from the fire, and prevents it from getting too hot.

The fire-grate is fixed 3 feet 2 inches below the roof of the fire-box, and 9 inches above the bottom, and is composed of separate loose bars of wrought iron, 2½ inches deep in the middle, and 1 inch thick at the upper side, tapering downwards to allow more free ingress for the air. The fire-bars are bent down at the ends, and drop into holes in a square frame of iron.

The fire-boxes, being flat on all sides except the top of the external one, are connected together by a number of ¾ inch copper bolts, which are screwed along their whole length and are passed through holes in both plates, tapped to receive them, and then riveted over at the ends for additional security. These copper bolts are screwed in, about 4 inches apart, all over the sides and back of the internal fire-box and that portion of the front that is below the boiler. The roof of the internal fire-box is strengthened by six wrought-iron ribs, placed parallel to each other and longitudinally upon the roof, and fastened to it by bolts screwed through the roof-plate, and having, in addition, a nut screwed on at the under side. A small plug of lead is put through a hole in the centre of the roof of the fire-box, and riveted over on both sides: when the water gets so low as to uncover this plug, it is melted by the heat, and the steam, rushing into the fire-box, extinguishes the fire.

Tubes

The communication between the fire-box and the chimney is made by a number of tubes, which are fixed water-tight at one end into the front plate of the fire-box, and at the other into the plate which closes the front end of the boiler. There are 124 of these tubes; they are $1^5/_8$ inch in diameter outside, and a space of ¾ inch is left between them. They are made of the best rolled brass, $1/_{13}$ of an inch thick, called No. 13 wire-gauge. The ends of the tubes are fixed by driving in a steel hoop or ferrule, made slightly conical. The ferrule is a little larger than the tube, so that, when driven in, it compresses the tube very forcibly against the sides of the hole, and makes the joint completely water-tight.

The tubes being firmly fixed into both ends of the boiler, serve to support and strengthen them; but, for an additional support to the upper part, six wrought-iron tie-rods are placed above the internal fire-box, by the side of each other, and longitudinally in the boiler; and the ends are attached by pins to a piece of wrought iron (T iron) riveted on to the end plate of the boiler and to the back plate of the fire-box.

Smoke-box

The Smoke-box is 4 feet wide, like the fire-box, and 2 feet long, and is closed on all sides; the back of it is formed by a wrought-iron plate, ½ inch thick, closing the end of the boiler, to which it is attached by means of a piece of angle-iron riveted to both, like the similar joint at the fire-box. The rest of the smoke-box is made of ¼ inch iron plates, riveted together, except the front plate, which is fixed by screw-bolts and nuts, because it is required occasionally to be taken off.

Upon the smoke-box is fixed the chimney; it is 15 inches in diameter, and is made of $1/8$ inch iron plates, riveted together and bound round by hoops; the top is made funnel-shaped, to give more free egress to the hot air.

In the lower part of the smoke-box are fixed the two cylinders, where the steam is used and motion is produced.

The tubes open into the upper part of the smoke-box, and the hot air passes from them up the chimney. The draught up the chimney is augmented by causing the waste steam to issue through the pipe called the blast-pipe, which is directed up into the centre of the chimney, and is gradually contracted throughout its length to make the steam rush out with more force: this pipe is made of copper $1/8$ of an inch thick, and is $3^3/4$ inches in diameter inside at the bottom, where it joins on to the cylinders, and tapers to 2½ inches at the top.

The force of the draught produced by the steam-blast is so great that cinders are drawn through the tubes, and even thrown red-hot out of the top of the chimney. Sparks are also emitted occasionally, and have sometimes caused accidents. To prevent the cinders and sparks from getting out of the chimney, a wire sieve was often fixed on the top of the chimney, but this had a disadvantage in impeding the draught and the exit of the waste steam very considerably; though it was made convex and larger than the chimney, so as to have a larger surface, and to impede the passage as little as possible. The sieve is, however, but an imperfect remedy, for the cinders are thrown against the sieve with so much force that the meshes are soon destroyed.

Damper

A damper is placed in the chimney just below the top of the blast-pipe, consisting of a thin iron plate fitting the chimney closely, with a hole cut in its centre, just large enough to allow the blast-pipe to pass through. It is swivelled on a spindle, fixed a little out of the centre, in order to clear the blast-pipe when the damper is elevated. The damper is used to check the draught when a less intense action of the fire is required, such as when the engine is standing still or running down hill, and very little power is wanted. It causes very little obstruction to the exit of the waste steam, as the blast-pipe passes through it.

Smoke-box Doors

A large door is made in the front plate of the smoke-box for the purpose of affording access to the cylinders and the tubes. There is also a small door, near the bottom of the smoke-box, for the purpose of clearing out cinders and ashes. Both doors have to fit closely, that no air may enter by them to impair the draught.

Gauges

A glass gauge is provided for showing the height of the water in the boiler; it is shown detached in Fig. 6, which is a section through the centre of it, to a scale of 2¼ inches to a foot, or three times the size of the engraving. The gauge consists of a strong glass tube, A, about ¾ inch diameter outside, fitted into a brass socket, B B, at top and bottom, the joints being made steam-tight by hemp packing put round the glass, and compressed against it by the glands, C C, which are screwed in round the glass. From each of the socket-pieces, B, a tube, D, proceeds, with a cock in it, and a screw on the end for fixing it into the fire-box; and the piece E, containing another cock, is screwed into the lower piece, and the plug F into the upper piece, affording the means of putting the glass tube down into its place. When the two cocks, D D, are opened, the water of the boiler rises in the glass tube to the same height that it is in the boiler, the upper part of the glass being filled with steam, the height of the water in it showing always the level of the water in the boiler. The cocks are for the purpose of stopping the communication when required, from the gauge being out of order or otherwise. The cock

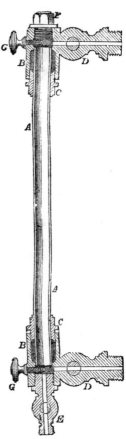

Figure 6. Glass Gauge.

in the piece E is for the purpose of clearing out the gauge by allowing a stream of water to run through it. A small plug, G, is screwed in opposite each tube D, to afford the means of clearing out the tubes D, by passing a wire through them when the plugs G are taken out.

To afford an additional means of ascertaining the height of the water in the boiler, two gauge-cocks are fixed in the side of the fire-box, one being 4 inches above the other, and the lower one 1 inch above the top of the internal fire-box.

Safety-valves

The pressure of steam in the boiler is regulated by the safety-valve, the construction of which is shown in Figs. 7. The valve, A, is made of brass: it is conical round the edge, or mitred at an angle of 45°, and has a spindle or stalk, B, cast on it in the middle, guided in a cross coil, D. The seat, C, of the valve is also of brass, and is cast with a flanch at the bottom, by which it is bolted on to the boiler; and the valve is ground into the upper part, so as to fit it steam-tight. The opening in the valve-seat, C, is 2½ inches diameter. A projecting lug, E, is cast on the valve-seat, in which is fixed the standard, F; this is forked at the top, and receives the end of the lever, G, which turns in it upon a centre pin; a rod, H, is jointed to the lever by another pin, at 3 inches from the former one, and bears directly upon the valve.

At the other end of the lever, and at a length of 3 feet from the fulcrum, is attached by a finger-nut the rod of a common spring balance, the bottom of which is fixed on to the fire-box: this spring balance is screwed up by the finger-nut by the valve lever, until the required pressure on the valve is produced, which is generally 50lbs on the square inch above the atmosphere; and the valve, on rising to let out the surplus steam, has to raise the spring balance, which acts upon it with twelve times the leverage.

A lock-up safety-valve is enclosed in a case, to prevent access to it so as to cause the pressure to be increased to a dangerous degree. The valve is held down by several small elliptical springs, about 6 inches long, placed one above another and over the valve, and pressed down by an adjusting screw at the top in the frame, fixed into the valve-seat.

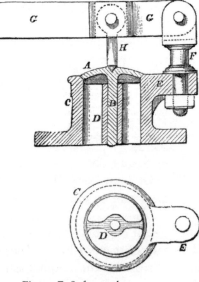

Figure 7. Safety-valve.

Man-hole

A circular opening into the boiler is provided, called the man-hole; it is 16 inches in diameter, and surrounded by a ring, bolted on to the boiler, having a flanch at the top for fixing on the cover. This opening is large enough for a man to enter, and affords access to the interior of the boiler for making repairs in it, or for cleaning it out.

Mud-holes

These are two small openings in both sides of the fire-box at the bottom, closed by plates bolted upon the outside, and are for the purpose of cleaning out the fire-box and removing the sediment that is deposited from the water.

Blow-off Cocks

Two cocks, 1 inch in diameter, are fixed one in each side of the fire-box, close to the bottom, for the purpose of emptying the boiler; this is called *blowing-off*, as it is done just after the engine has left work, and the water is blown out with great force by the pressure of the steam. This blowing-off serves to cleanse the boiler.

Fire and Heating Power

The area of the fire-grate is 9½ square feet; it is 18 inches below the bottom of the lowest tubes, and the space for the fire, when quite filled up to the tubes, is 14 cubic feet, and holds about 2½cwt of coke; but the fire-box is not always filled so full as this, and usually contains about 1½ or 2cwt.

The surface of water exposed to the heat directly radiated from the fire, is the whole surface of the internal firebox, deducting the fire-door and the tubes, and is equal to 50 square feet; and that exposed to the current of hot air, or conducted heat, is the interior surface of the tubes, and is equal to 432 square feet.

Steam-pipe

A steam-pipe is provided for conveying the steam from the boiler to the cylinder, where it is to be used; it is made of copper $^3/_{16}$ths of an inch thick, and the part within the boiler is 5 inches diameter inside; it passes through the tube-plate of the smoke-box and is bolted to it by a flanch. The pipe then divides into two smaller ones, 3½ inches in diameter, which pass down on each side of the smoke-box to the cylinders; they are turned on one side in order to keep them clear of the tubes, so as to allow access to all the tubes, that they may be taken out, when necessary, through the smoke-box door.

The steam enters through a funnel-shaped copper pipe, which is fixed upon the top of the steam-box, from which the main steam-pipe is supplied; this pipe rises nearly to the top of the steam-dome, which is made of brass, $^3/_8$ inch thick, 15 inches in diameter, and 2 feet high, and bolted to the fire-box. The object of this steam-dome, and of carrying the steam-pipe up to the top of it, is to obtain the steam as pure and dry as possible, by taking it at a distance from the water; because, from the great agitation of the water in the boiler, and the rapid emission of the steam to the cylinders, some of the water gets mixed up with the steam in a finely divided state, and is liable to pass over with the steam into the cylinders.

Regulator
In the box is placed the regulator, Figs. 8, by means of which the steam is either shut off or allowed to enter the steam-pipe in greater or less quantities. The box has a plate, A, extending across it, with two openings, B B, of nearly a quadrant each. The brass plate, C, of a corresponding form, is placed against this plate, and is kept in contact with it by the pressure of the steam. It is turned on the face, A, to which it is pivoted, by the spindle, D, and so regulates the amount of the openings, B B, for steam, or closes them entirely.

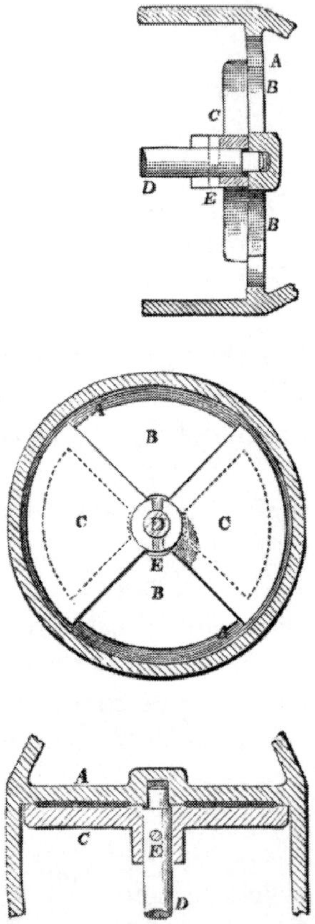

Valve-chests
The valve-chests are bolted down, one upon the top of each cylinder. They have two branches of the steam-pipe fixed upon them at the back, and opening into them; and a stuffing-box is cast upon the end of each, passing through the tube-plate, the joint being completely and firmly closed by running melted lead into it all round.

Slide-valves
In the valve-chests are placed the slide-valves. They are brass boxes 1½ inch deep inside, and

Figure 8. Regulator.

$^3/_8$ of an inch thick, having flanches $^5/_8$ of an inch thick all round them at the bottom. The slide-valves are made to move backwards and forwards by spindles, which have each a cross piece at the end that fits into a notch in the back of the valve; the spindle is generally connected to the valve by means of a rectangular wrought-iron frame called a bridle, placed over the valve, and having the spindle screwed into it. The bridle has an advantage in holding the valve very steady, and yet allowing it to drop through readily, as it is worn by friction, and thus keep always in contact with the surface that it slides upon. The valve-spindle moves steam-tight through the stuffing-box at the inner end of the steam-chest.

Cylinders and Pistons

The cylinders, in which motion is produced by the pressure of the steam, are made of cast-iron, $5/8$ of an inch thick, and bored out to 12 inches in diameter. From each end of the cylinders, a steam-passage is brought, and terminates in a flat face on the top of the cylinder, forming the bottom of the valve-chest. A third passage is constructed between the two steam-passages, to serve as an exhaust-passage, or way of escape for the waste or exhaust steam. Each steam-port, or entrance to the steam-passage, is 8 inches long and 1 inch wide, and the exhaust port is 1½ inch wide and 8 inches long. These passages, A, B, and C, Fig. 9, are brought up to one flat surface, that they may be simply opened and closed for the ingress and the egress of the steam to and from the cylinder by a flat-faced box, or slide, or valve, F G, which is moved forwards and backwards, and on the face, by a regular alternate movement. The ports are separated by the bars, D D. When the valve is in its central position over the ports, shown by dot-lining, the two ends of the valve cover the steam-ports, A and B, completely, and a little over. The amount by which it is over at each port is called *lap*, and in this instance the inside lap is $1/16$ inch at each port, and the outside lap is also $1/16$ inch at each port. The valve is shown fully open for the admission of steam to the port B, and for the exhaust or escape of steam from the port a through the port C.

The slide-valve is moved backwards and forwards a distance of 3 inches, or 1½ inch on each side of the central position, and is carried beyond the inner edge of each steam-port alternately, a distance of nearly ½ an inch, as shown in Fig. 9, before its motion is changed and it begins to move back again: this distance traversed by the slide is called 'the travel.' The exhaust-port is always covered by the slide, as the travel is less than the width of the bars, so that the steam is always prevented from entering the waste-port from the valve-chest. During the reciprocating motion of the slide, each of the steam-ports is alternately

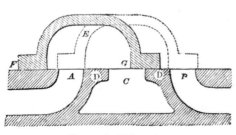

Figure 9. Slide-valve.

uncovered, and the steam allowed to enter and flow into the cylinder. The port is then covered again by the slide, and, when the flanch has passed over, it communicates through the inside of the slide with the waste steam-port, allowing the steam which has performed its duty in the cylinder to escape, by the port at which it had entered, into the waste-port and out at the blast-pipe; this action is called 'the eduction'. The slide-valve is held upon the face of the ports only by the pressure of the steam upon it, which is quite sufficient to keep it always steam-tight whilst moving, as the inside of the slide is open to the atmospheric pressure only, through the waste-port, and the flanches fit air-tight upon the face of the ports; so that the whole pressure of the steam upon the slide is effective in keeping it down. The area of the slide being 55 square inches, the pressure upon it is about 1¼ ton.

The front end of each of the cylinders runs through the plate of the smoke-box, projecting beyond it, and having a flanch resting against the inside of the plate, and fixed to it by bolts, which are screwed through the plate into the flanch. The cylinder-cover, ⅞ inch thick, is of the same size as this flanch, and is held on to the cylinder by the same bolts that fix the cylinder to the smoke-box plate. The back end of the cylinder has also a flanch, by which it is bolted to the inside of the tube-plate : this is shown on a large scale in Figs. 10, which are a longitudinal and a cross section of the cylinder. O O is a section of the cylinder; P P the back steam-port leading into the end of the cylinder; Q Q is the tube-plate or back plate of the smoke-box; and R, the flanch upon the cylinder, similar to that at the other end. The cylinder passes through the plate, and comes flush with the outside; the joints and the space between the flanch and the plate are run with lead all round, to make the cylinder quite firm and steady, as the hole in the plate does not accurately fit the cylinder; the joint at the other end of the cylinder is also run flush with lead for the same reason. The flanch is fixed to the plate by six ¾ inch bolts, which are screwed into the flanch from the outside, in order that they may fit closely to the holes in the flanch and the plate, and hold the cylinder quite steady. A flanch, S S, is cast on the inside of the end of the cylinder, projecting into the cylinder, and the cover, T, is bolted to the outside of this flanch. There is one piston in each cylinder, 3½ inches thick, made of brass, and consisting of a plate, A, having a boss, B, with three arms, C C C, cast on it, with another plate, D, fixed by screws, E E E. The plates A and D are turned to such a diameter as to be just capable of moving in the cylinder without touching it, and three brass rings, F F, are placed between them. The inner ring is ⅜ inch thick, and is of the same width as the space between the plates: the two outer rings are ½ an inch thick, and of half the width; and one of them has a projecting ring or rebate upon

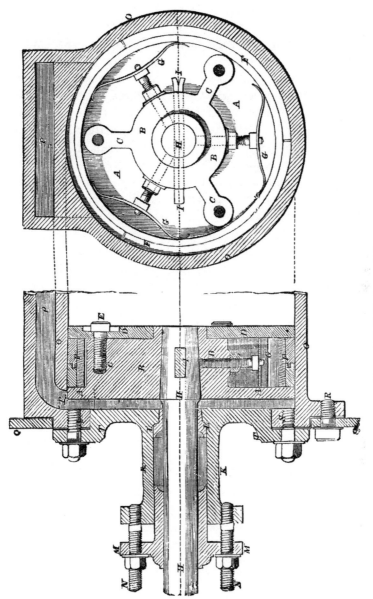

Figure 10. Cylinder and Piston.

its edge, fitting into a corresponding groove in the other to keep them steady. The rings are turned exactly to fit the cylinder and each other, and cut through in one part, having been first hammered a little all round on the inside, which gives them a tendency to expand, and causes them to fly open on being cut. When, therefore, they are put in their places in the cylinder, they press against the cylinder by their elasticity, and keep in close contact with it, so as to make a steam-tight joint during the motion of the piston. They are tightened, when it becomes necessary by wear, by means of three steel springs, G G G, placed in the piston. The piston-rod is of steel, 1¾ inch diameter, and is made conical at the end; fixed to the piston by a cotter, split at the end to prevent its getting loose. The other end of the piston-rod passes through the stuffing-box, K, Figs. 10, in the cylinder-cover. The stuffing-box has ½ inch space round the piston-rod for the packing which rests against the brass ring or bush, L, fitted on to a small flanch at the end of the stuffing-box, and is compressed by the brass gland, M, which leaves about 3 inches for the packing. The gland is held by bolts to the stuffing-box.

Since the operations of admission, cutting-off, and exhaust of the steam from each end of the cylinder, are effected by the simple reciprocating movement of the slide-valve, properly timed, over the three-ported face of the cylinder, it follows that they may be effected with the utmost degree of precision by driving the valve from the engine itself. This is done by means of the valve-gear. The action is consecutively as follows: Steam is admitted to one end of the cylinder when the piston has arrived there, and it follows the piston till it arrives nearly at the other end of the cylinder. It is then shut off by the valve, and the steam, thus shut in, expands behind the piston for a little way, and is finally exhausted in consequence of the movement of the valve, which uncovers the steam-port and opens a way for the confined steam into the exhaust-passage and the blast-pipe. But, though the greater proportion of the steam has thus been promptly evacuated, the cylinder remains filled with steam of a low pressure, equal to that of the atmosphere, or a little more. While, therefore, the piston returns to the first end of the cylinder, the valve, though constantly in motion, maintains open the communication between that end and the exhaust, and thus enables the atmospheric steam to pass out in advance of the returning piston, until the piston has nearly completed the return-*stroke*. At the end of the return-stroke and the beginning of the next stroke, steam, by the valve's motion, is again admitted from the valve-chest into the same end of the cylinder, and so the circuit is repeated. The same cycle of performance takes place for the other end of the cylinder, and the other face of the piston.

Crosshead and Connecting-rod

The power generated in the cylinders by the reciprocating motion of the pistons under the active pressure of the steam, is transmitted to the driving-axle by means of two connecting-rods, one to each cylinder. One end of each connecting-rod, attached to the end of the piston-rod, travels to and fro in a straight line; the other end revolves upon, and with, a crank on the revolving axle. So simple and effective is the means of transforming rectilineal into circular motion. To make the needful attachment to the piston-rod, A, it is fitted with a crosshead, G B G, shown in Figs. 11, in which a socket B is keyed on the end of the piston-rod, A, by the gib, D, and cotter, C. To the forks, E E, the crosshead, F, 1¾ inch in diameter, is fastened by means of straps, G G, fixed each with a gib, I, and cotter, H. The crosshead is guided by two slide-blocks, L, one at each end, 6 inches long, which slide between parallel guide-bars of steel, M N, 2½ inches wide, fixed by angle-irons, O O, to the framing, R, R. On the spherical enlargement, W, of the crosshead the small end, S, of the connecting-rod, 1⅝ inch in diameter, is applied. For this purpose, it is enlarged at T to a width of 3 inches, and fitted with brasses, U V, 2 inches wide, taking their

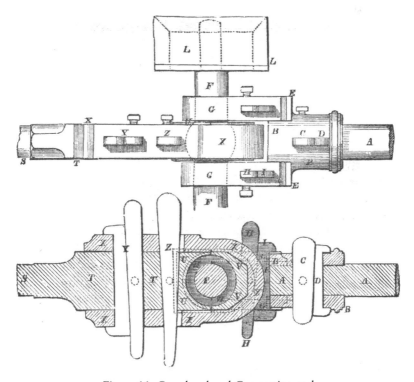

Figure 11. Crosshead and Connecting-rod.

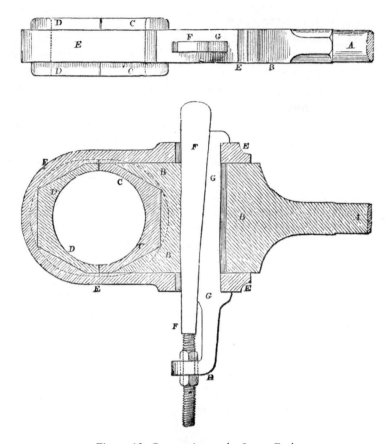

Figure 12. Connecting-rod – Large End.

bearing on the ball. The strap, X, surrounding the brasses, is fixed fast to the connecting-rod by the gib and cotter, Y, whilst the brasses are brought up to their bearings by the independent cotter, Z. Every cotter is secured in its position by a set-screw applied laterally. The other end, A, of the connecting-rod, Figs. 12, is enlarged at B to a width of 5¾ inches. The brasses, C D, are octagonal, and are bored out to a diameter of 5 inches, to embrace the crank-pin, or cranked portion of the axle. The brasses are held by the strap, E, secured by the gib, G, and the cotter, F. The cotter terminates as a screw which passes through a hole in the gib-piece, and is secured in position by two nuts.

Cranked Axle

The cranked axle, or driving-axle, is formed with two double-cranks, one for each cylinder, placed at right angles to each other, so that, when either piston is at the end of its stroke, the other piston is at the middle of its stroke. Thus a practically uniform propelling action is derived.

Excentrics

The reciprocating movements of the valves are derived from excentrics, which are fixed on the crank-axle, having an excentricity or throw of 1½ inch, making a total travel of 3 inches, which is communicated to each valve. Each valve is served by two excentrics, one for moving ahead and the other for reversing or moving backward, making in all four fixed excentrics. They are 10 inches in diameter, and are shown in Figs. 13, made in two parts, C D, fixed together across the axle, A, by two pins, F F, screwed into the piece, C, and cottered. They are made fast on the axle by the key, G. The brass ring, H H, surrounds the excentric; it is in two halves, united by flanches, I I, through which the fork-ends, K K, of the excentric-rod is passed and is fastened by nuts. Thus the excentric is free to revolve with the axle, inside the ring or excentric-strap, and communicates the reciprocating movement horizontally to the excentric-rod and the valve.

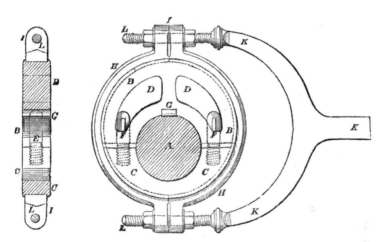

Figure 13. Excentric and Excentric-strap.

Slide-valve Gear

A side elevation of the excentric-rods and levers for working the slide for one cylinder is shown detached in Fig. 14. The excentric, E', is for working the slide when the engine is running forward; and the end of the excentric-rod, e'', is formed into a large vertical fork, g'', having a notch in the bottom. This notch takes hold of a steel pin, with shoulders to hold the excentric-rod steadily, which is fixed into the lower end of the lever, h'', by means of a nut screwed on at the other side. The lever, h'', is keyed on to the end of the horizontal shaft or weigh-bar, i'', turning in brass carriages fixed on to the frame of the engine. Upon the weigh-bar, i'', and standing above, is fixed the lever, l''; and a horizontal link, m'', is attached to the end of the lever by a steel pin passed through it; the other end of the link m'' being attached in a similar manner to a socket on the valve spindle l'.

The excentric-rod e'', taking hold of the lever h'', makes it move backwards and forwards with the excentric; and the top lever l'' communicates the motion to the valve-spindle by means of the link m''. The levers h'' and l'' being of the same length, the motion of the slide-valves is the same as the double-throw of the excentrics, or 3 inches, as before stated. The excentric is fixed in such a position, with regard to the crank, that the port is full open, or the slide at the end of its motion, when the piston is at half stroke, as shown in the diagram. The excentrics are, therefore, at right angles to their respective cranks, and they have to be fixed a quarter of a revolution behind the cranks, in order to move the slides as much in advance of the pistons; because the levers h'' and l'' reverse the motion, so that when the slide has to be pulled back, the excentric-rod must be pushed forward.

Reversing Gear

The excentrics, E', are placed so as to work the engine forward, and when the crank is down to cause the piston to be pushed back, and pulled forward when above the axle, and thus cause the wheels to turn round in the direction of the arrow, and propel the engine forward. In order to make the engine run in the opposite direction, another excentric, F', is necessary for each cylinder, which is placed exactly in an opposite direction to the former one, or at the extreme back position, when the former one is at its maximum travel forward. Its rod f'' has a fork at the end, similar to the other excentric-rod; and a lever corresponding to it is fixed on the other end of the weigh-bar i'', exactly like the lever h''. The two excentric-rods have pins fixed into them below the forks, and attached to the suspending-rods, o'' o'''; the middle rod, o'', for the working excentric, E', being connected at the top to a cross-head at the end of the horizontal lever, p'', and the other, o''', for the reversing excentric, forked at the top, and attached to the lever, p''', which extends in the opposite direction to the lever p''. The lever p'' is keyed upon the cross-shaft q'', and the other, p''', upon another shaft, q''', both extending to the side of the engine, and turning in carriages, and having the vertical levers, r'' r''', fixed upon their outer ends. The levers, r'' r''', are connected by the link, $8''$, attached to both; and one of them, r'', extends above the joint, and is attached to the end of the long bar, t'', extending to the back of the engine, and connected to a similar lever upon a short shaft, which is fixed on the frame at the side of the fire-box. On the outer end of this shaft, and close to the hand-railing of the engine, is fixed the long handle or reversing-lever, which moves between guide-plates attached to the hand-rail; the outer guide having a notch in the middle to hold the lever in a vertical position, and another at each extremity of the passage between the guide-plates.

In Fig. 14 the reversing lever is supposed to be pushed over into the forward notch, pulling the levers, r'' r''', forward also by the bar, t'', and link, $8''$, causing the lever, p'', to be raised by the means of the cross-shaft, q'', and to pull up the end of the excentric-rod, e'', by the suspending-rod, o'', making the notch in it take hold of the pin in the bottom lever, h'', of the weigh-bar. The two forward working excentrics, E', are thus put into gear, and made to work the slides of the two cylinders, and cause the engine to be propelled forwards. The other lifting lever, p''', is at the same time lowered by the lever, r''', being pulled forward, letting down the rod, f'', of the reversing excentric by the suspending-rod, o''', so that the fork clears entirely the pin in the levers, n'', leaving it free to move with the weigh-bar, and in an exactly opposite direction to the excentric-rod, f'', below it.

When the hand-lever is placed in the centre notch of the guides, or in a vertical position, side lever r'' is brought upright, and the lifting lever p'' made horizontal; so that the ends of the middle excentric-rods are let down, and the notches in them escape from the pins in the bottom levers of the weigh-bars; and the outside excentric-rods, f' f'', are only raised into a similar position, and are still not in contact with the levers of the weigh-bars. The slides will therefore cease to be worked, although the excentric-rods continue moving, and the engine will not be propelled anymore as the steam continues pressing upon the same sides of the pistons.

But when the hand-lever is pulled quite over into the back notch of the guides, the positions of the excentric-rods are reversed. The reversing

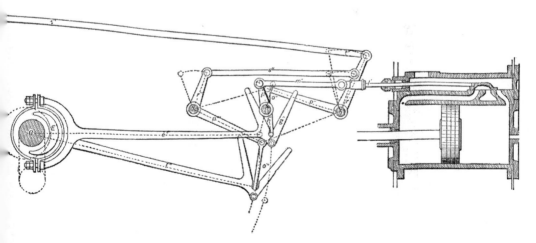

Figure 14. Valve-gear for one Cylinder.

excentrics are thus brought into gear and made to work the slides, causing the motion of the pistons to be reversed by the steam being admitted on the opposite side of them, and making the engine run in the opposite direction to its former course; the middle excentric-rod, *e"*, is at the same time lowered, as the outside one was before, allowing the fork upon it to clear the pin of the lever, *h"*. The engine can then be propelled forward again, by putting the hand-lever over into its front position, dropping the rods of the outer reversing excentrics out of gear, and drawing up the inner rods of the forward working excentrics, to force the levers of the weigh-bars into the opposite positions by their forks, and take hold of the pins in them.

The engine can thus be made to run either forward or backward by merely pulling the hand-lever forward or back; and the handle is placed close to the engine-man, who stands behind the fire-box, so as to be readily moved.

All the moving parts require a constant supply of oil to diminish the friction; and oil-cups are fixed for this purpose upon all the principal moving parts, such as on the ends of the connecting-rods over the bearings, on each of the piston-rod guides, and over the piston-rod and the slide-valve spindle; the piston is oiled by pouring oil into the cylinder by the cock in the cylinder-cover, the bent end of the cock turning round for the purpose. An oil-cup is shown, one-quarter the full size, in Figs. 15, showing a side elevation of it, a section through the centre, and a plan of the top. The cup, A, is made of brass, and the cover, B, is hinged to it, with a spring to hold it either open or shut. An iron tube, D, is fixed into the foot of the cup, extending to the top, and projecting through the bottom, where it is screwed, for the purpose of fixing the cup on to the part which is to be oiled. The hole into which the cup is screwed runs through to the rubbing surface; and some cotton thread is put through the tube, dipping into the oil in the cup, and the other end touching the moving part; the thread acts as a syphon, and continually drops the oil upon the rubbing surface. The oil-cup on the crank-end of the connecting-rod has so violent a motion that it is almost impossible to keep the cover shut, unless the spring is very strong. The covers are sometimes detached and screwed on, but they are then very liable to be lost; and the best cup for that purpose was found to be one without a loose cover, but with

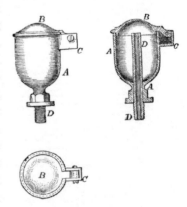

Figure 15. Oil-cup.

only a small hole in the top to pour in the oil, and made funnel-shape inside to prevent the oil jolting out of the hole.

Feed-pumps

The feed-pumps are fixed by means of flanches to plates, which are bolted on to the frame of the engine. Each pump is worked by an arm, fitted on to the piston-rod and attached at the outer end to the plunger of the pump. The barrel of the pump, A A, Figs. 16, is made of cast iron, 1¾ inch in diameter inside, and ³/₈ inch thick, B B is the plunger, 1⅝ inch in diameter, and made of a wrought-iron tube for the sake of lightness, plugged up at the inner end, and having a short rod keyed into the other end, which is fixed into the socket in the driving arm by a nut screwed on the end. The plunger, B, passes through a stuffing-box, C, at the end of the pump-barrel, A, with a brass gland, D, attached by screws, E E, to the flanch of the stuffing-box.

The end of the pump is closed by a screwed plug, F, to afford access to the interior. To the short cross pieces, G G, the brass tubes, L, I, and M, are bolted, holding the valves, which are true spheres, confined in cages, Q R, with a certain degree of free vertical lift, for the passage of water, arriving by the pipe, H, connected by the union, K, to the branch, i, and departing by the upper branch, M, connected by the union, O, to the delivery-pipe, N, which carries the water to the boiler. The upper cage, R, is held in position against the upward rush of the water from the pump by a pinching screw, V, locked with a nut, W. The suction-pipe, H, passes under the fire-box, and is connected at the end to one of the pipes that bring the water from the tender.

The plunger, B, Figs. 16, is worked in and out of the barrel of the pump, A, a distance of 18 inches, by the piston-rod, at each stroke, leaving a space behind it when drawn out equal to its bulk, which is supplied with water through the suction-pipe and lower valve, and the water again forced out through the upper valve and delivery-pipe into the boiler when the plunger is pushed in. The internal diameter of the suction and delivery pipes, and of the water-way in the valve-seats, is 1 inch. The pump would force a quantity of water into the boiler at each stroke, equal to the bulk of the plunger, for 18 inches in length, if the suction-pipes were kept open; but the quantity is regulated according to circumstances, by means of cocks fixed in the suction-pipes, the handles of which extend upwards through the foot-board on which the engine-man stands, so as to be within his reach. The closing of these cocks causes the plunger to leave a partial vacuum behind it, and as the water cannot enter to fill it up, so much less water is forced into the boiler.

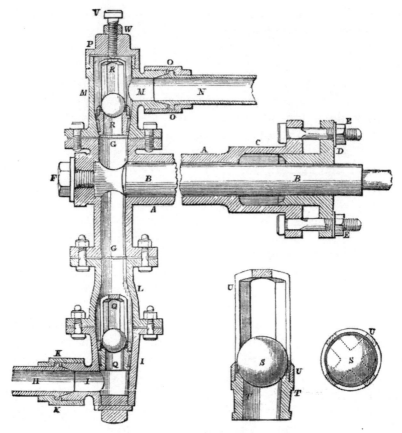

Figure 16. Feed-pump.

Wheels

The wheels are of two kinds: the two driving-wheels, which are fixed on the crank-axle, are 5 feet in diameter and are flat on the edge; the other four wheels, two of them placed towards the front, just behind the smoke-box, and the other two, at the back behind the fire-box, are 3 feet 6 inches in diameter, and have a projecting rim or flanch upon their edges, which runs against the inner side of the rails. Each pair of the small wheels is fixed upon an axle, as well as the large wheels; they are $3^5/8$ inches in diameter, and the outer ends project beyond the wheels, turning in brasses in the frame of the engine. Upon these brasses the whole weight of the engine rests through the medium of the springs above them; and all the weight is thus suspended by springs, except that of the wheels and axles themselves, for the purpose of deadening the shocks that are caused in the rapid motion of the engine.

The construction of the wheels is shown in Figs. 17 and 18. A A is the axle of each wheel, with outside bearings, B B. C C are the naves of

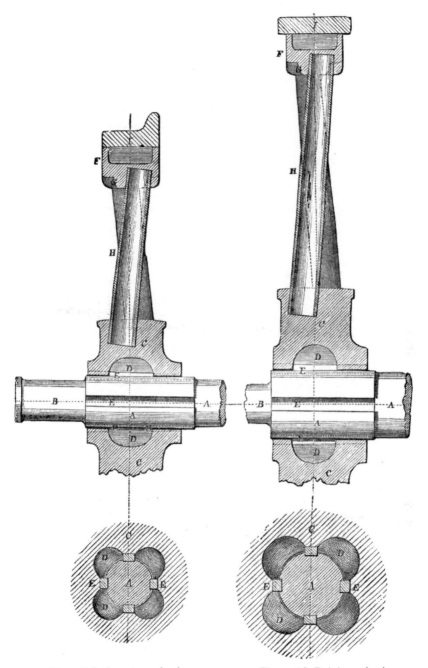

Figure 17. Carrying-wheels.   Figure 18. Driving-wheels.

the wheels, made of cast iron; and they are fixed by four keys, E E, each driven into grooves cut in the axles and inside the naves.

The rim of the wheels, F F, are of cast iron, 4½ inches wide and 2½ inches deep. The spokes, H H, are wrought-iron tubes ¼ inch thick, and tapering from 2¼ inches to 2 inches in diameter, and they are cast in the nave and rim. I I are the tires of the wheels; they are made of wrought-iron rolled into the required shape, with the ends welded together; the plain one, for the driving-wheels, is 5¾ inches wide, and the flanch-tire, for the small wheels, 4½ inches wide. They are both made slightly conical, being tapered from $1^{3}/_{8}$ inch to 1½-inch thick; and the flanch projects 1¼ inch, and is ¾ inch thick at the edge, and 1 inch thick at the base. The rims and tires are both turned, and the tires arc heated when put on, and contract in cooling, so as to hold firmly on the wheel.

Outside Framing, &c.

The principal or outside frame is placed along the sides of the engine outside the wheels, and across the ends, serving to support the whole engine, which is firmly fixed to it. It is made of good tough ash plank; the side pieces are 3 inches thick and 7 inches deep, and covered on both sides with wrought-iron plates, ¼ inch thick, fixed on by a number of iron bolts. The end piece of the frame in front is 5 inches thick, and 13 inches deep: angle pieces of iron are bolted on, to strengthen the corners inside and out. The outside length of the frame is 17 feet, and the width 6 feet

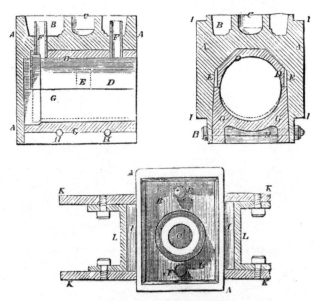

Figure 19. Axle-boxes.

4 inches. The boiler, fire-box, and smoke-box are fixed to the side frames by strong wrought-iron stays.

Wrought-iron plates, $7/16$ of an inch thick, are bolted on to each side of the frame at the axles, and called the axle-guards, serving to hold steadily the boxes that contain the brasses bearing on the axles, and to guide them when they slide up and down from the play of the springs.

The axle-boxes in which the axles turn are all alike and are shown in Figs. 19, comprising a section along the centre of one of them; a cross section; and a plan of the top. A A is a cast-iron box, open at the bottom and the inner side, and 4½ inches wide, so as to fit into the opening in the axle-guides.

The hollow, B, holds a supply of oil for lubrication; the hollow, C, receives the spindle supporting the spring. The brass bearing, D, fits with a small projection, E, on each side into a notch in the sides of the box. The oil is syphoned by cotton thread through two brass tubes, F F. The bottom is closed by the cast-iron piece, G G, sustained by the cross bolts and nuts. The sliding surfaces of the box, I I, bear upon the guides, L L, secured to the axle-guards.

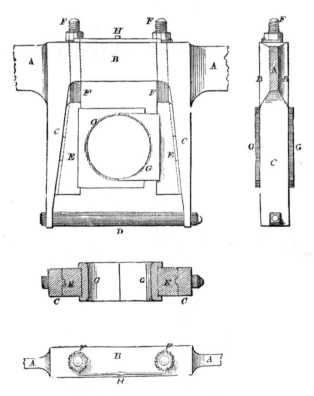

Figure 20. Inside Axle-bearings.

The springs are of steel plates $^5/_{16}$ inch in thickness. The buffers at the front end are leather cushions stuffed with horsehair.

Inside Frames

Four wrought-iron frames, 3½ inches deep and ¾ inch thick, are fixed between the smoke-box and fire-box, to afford additional strength to the engine by securing firmly the back plate of the smoke-box in which the cylinders are fixed, and which has to bear the whole strain of the working of the engine. These inside frames have also bearings in them for the cranked axle, and hold it steadily against the action of the connecting-rods, by which it is strained alternately in opposite directions. They are attached to the smoke-box and fire-box by means of T-shaped pieces of iron, which are riveted on to their inner and side plates, and are bolted to the ends of the frames; the two middle frames are made to approach each other, and are welded together at the back end, so that there are only three bearings on the cranked axle.

The inside bearings, shown in Figs. 20, are formed by thickening the frame-plate, A, to 2¼ inches at B; it is made with two inclined limbs, and between which are placed the two brasses G G, C C, by which the axle is embraced. These are tightened and adjusted by means of wedges, E E, taken up by screws and nuts, F F. The lower ends of the fork are united by a tube, D, placed between them, and a bolt and nut passed through it.

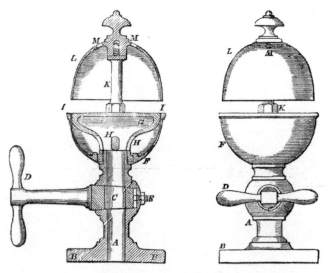

Figure 21. Steam-whistle.

Whistle

A steam-whistle, Figs. 21, is used for the purpose of giving warning of the approach of the engine when running. It is all of brass, and the foot, A, is cast hollow, with a flanch, B, at the bottom to bolt it upon the fire-box: it has a cock, C, with the handle, D. Between the cup, F, and the block, G, steam from the orifices, H, escapes at the circumference, I I, and strikes the thin edge of the bell, L, so as to produce an exceedingly shrill sound.

The Tender

The tender is attached behind the engine and close to it; it contains a tank of water for supplying the boiler, and has a space in the middle filled with coke for feeding the fire.

Tank

The water-tank is made of wrought-iron plates ½ inch thick, of a horse-shoe shape, 9 feet long, 6¾ feet wide, and 2¼ feet deep. A copper pipe from each end of the tank is connected to a hose-pipe. The two hose-pipes are attached to the suction-pipes, for the feed-pumps of the engine, by screwed sockets or union joints, which can be readily unfastened when the tender has to be separated from the engine.

Coke

The middle space of the tender is occupied with coke, the front end being made level with the foot-board of the engine, and a board fixed inclining from thence down to the floor for the convenience of taking up the coke with a shovel to throw it upon the fire: the bottom and sides are covered with sheet-iron.

Brake

The Brake for stopping the wheels consists of two wrought-iron frames, hung by pins from the side frame of the tender, and having blocks of wood fixed on to them, that are cut to fit the circumference of the wheels. A flat iron wedge fits into grooves in the two frames, and is continued up by a rod to the top of the tender, passing through a strong iron piece, and having a double handle screwed upon it. By screwing down the handle the wedge is drawn gradually up, and the two brakes are separated from each other, pressing the wood of each very forcibly against the wheels until they are stopped, if necessary.

Up to the year 1839,[1] thirty-seven six-wheel engines appear to have been put on the Liverpool and Manchester Railway, the driving-wheels

---

1. Very much of what follows on the Historical Progress of the Locomotive was abstracted by Mr Dempsey from *Railway Machinery,* 1855.

being 5 feet in diameter, and the four carrying-wheels 3 feet 6 inches. The cylinders of some of these engines had been increased to 14 inches diameter, and the stroke to 20 inches. The weights of the engines, in working order, had grown to more than 15 tons in some cases, while their speed and power had been so greatly advanced that their average duty was to draw loads from 150 to 188 tons at 20½ miles per hour. Their consumption of coke in performing this duty varied from .26 to .34lb. per ton per mile. Loaded to the extent of 25 tons, these engines attained about 30 miles per hour, and consumed from .885 to 1.3lb. of coke per ton per mile. The quantity of water they evaporated for each pound of coke consumed varied from 6 to 7.5lbs.

On the Great Western Railway, the increased gauge of the line (or width between the rails, 7 feet), and heavier carriages and loads to be impelled, at once afforded the means of introducing wider and more powerful engines than on the ordinary gauge (4 feet 8½ inches), and rendered this accession of power necessary. Forty locomotives were supplied on this railway to the year 1840, and all of these, excepting one only, had six wheels. The driving-wheels of these engines varied from 6 to 10 feet in diameter, and the carrying-wheels from 3 feet 6 inches to 4 feet 6 inches. One of these engines, named the 'Morning Star' (built by Messrs. E. Stephenson and Co), had cylinders of 16 inches stroke and 16 inches diameter. The boiler was 8 feet 6 inches in length, 4 feet in diameter, and contained 169 tubes of $1^5/_8$ inch diameter, exposing an area equal to 648 feet to the contact of the heated air. The fire-box, 3 feet 5¼ inches long, 4 feet wide, and 3 feet 10½ inches high over the fire-bars, provided a surface for the action of the fire equal to 68½ superficial feet. The weight of the 'Morning Star' in working trim was described as being 12 tons 12 cwts 2 qrs. The duty of the 'North Star', another similar engine, built by the same engineers, was reported to be 184 tons load, exclusive of engine and tender, at the rate of 32½ miles per hour, for a distance (London to Maidenhead) of 22½ miles.

The London and Birmingham Railway retained the use of four-wheeled engines till the year 1845, the locomotive superintendent of the line, Mr Edward Bury, deeming them preferable to six-wheeled engines. The advantages of the former were described by Mr Bury to be as follows:– 'The four-wheeled engine is less costly than that on six wheels; it can be got into less space; is much lighter, and therefore requires less power to take it up the inclines, and consequently leaves more available power to take up the train; is safer, as it adapts itself better to the rails, not being so likely to run off the lines at curves or crossings; is more economical in the working, there being fewer parts in motion and less friction; those parts of the machinery which are common to both plans are more easily got at in the four-wheeled engine; the buildings and turntables are not required to be on so large a scale; as there are fewer parts in the four-wheeled engine, fewer tools, as lathes, drills, &c, are required; having fewer parts to be deranged, stoppages are not so likely to take place on the journey.' Experience, however, was demonstrating that, for high speeds, great loads, and severe gradients, four-wheeled engines were not so advantageous as those on six wheels; and when Mr Bury's superintendence of the department ceased, the latter description of engine became adopted on the London and Birmingham Railway, as it had long previously been, for general passenger traffic, on most other railways. In August 1845, the stock of engines on the London and Birmingham consisted of 89 four-wheeled and 1 six-wheeled. The four-wheeled engines had cylinders from 12 to 14 inches in diameter, and 18 inches stroke; the driving-wheels, 5 feet 6 inches to 6 feet diameter; and the usual weight of the engines, when charged, was from 10½ to 12½ tons. The largest four-wheeled engines had 14 inch cylinders, and weighed 13 tons empty. The six-wheeled engines of that period may he illustrated by Figs. 22 and 23, which represent the side elevation and cross section of one of the best description.

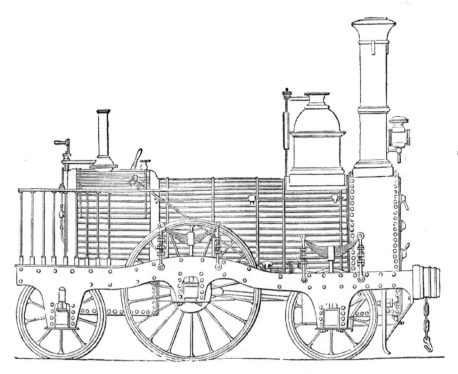

Figure 22. Six-wheeled Passenger Locomotive, 1845.

The railway between Birmingham and Gloucester having been constructed with a very steep gradient, the 'Lickey' Incline, of which the inclination for a length of 2 miles and 2.35 chains is 1 in 37, some locomotive engines for working the traffic up this incline were ordered from Philadelphia. These engines had a pair of driving-wheels 4 feet in diameter, and 4 front wheels, 2 feet 6 inches in diameter, attached to a 'bogie' or swivel frame under the smoke-box, the wheels being thus attached with a view of enabling the engine frame to adapt itself to curves. The cylinders were inclined in position, 10½ inches diameter and 18 inches stroke. The boilers had 78 tubes of 2 inches outside diameter, and 8 feet in length. These engines weighed about 8 tons when empty, or 9½ tons when charged. Converted into tank engines, their weight was augmented to about 14 tons. Their usual performance up the 'Lickey' was 33 tons at 12 to 15 miles per hour; 39½ tons at 10½ miles; or a maximum load of 53¼ tons at 8½ miles. On the Grand

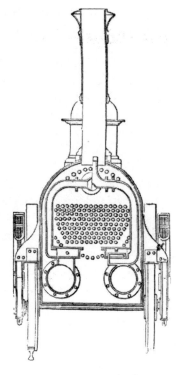

Figure 23. Six-wheel Locomotive, 1845. Section through Cylinders.

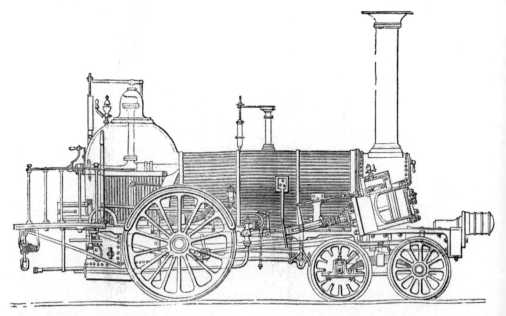

Figure 24. Bogie Engine similar to those constructed for the Birmingham and Gloucester Railway.

Junction Railway, Captain Moorsom reported that some of the American 'bogie' engines propelled loads of 100 to 120 tons on an incline of 1 in 330 at 14 to 22½ miles per hour; or on an incline of 1 in 177 at 10 to 14 miles per hour. The mean of seven journeys from Birmingham to Liverpool, with gross loads of about 100 tons, showed a consumption of 50lbs of coke per mile, and an evaporation of 4.27lbs of water per pound of coke. A 'bogie' engine of this character is represented in Fig. 24, in which the cylinders, &c, are shown in section.

On the Grand Junction Railway, opened in 1837, and the South-Western, opened in 1838, the engineer, Mr Joseph Locke, introduced locomotive engines which comprised several improvements in the details, due, it is believed, to Mr Allan, of Crewe. These comprised the removal of the cylinders to the outer sides of the smoke-box; the extension of the inside framing to the front end or buffer-beam of the engine, and the abandonment of outside bearings for the driving-axle; the attachment of the cylinders direct to the extended frames; the direct connection of the piston-rod with a pin in the nave of the driving-wheel; the complete removal of the inside cranks, leaving the excentrics and valve-gear only to be arranged beneath the boiler; and involving, necessarily, inside bearings for all the axles. Subsequently it was suggested to retain an outside framing, making it of a single ½ inch boiler plate on each side. The original locomotives constructed for the Grand Junction Railway, constructed in 1837, were six-wheeled, having inside cylinders from 12½ to 14 inches diameter and 18 inches stroke; boiler, 8 feet long, weighing from 9½ to 15 tons, when charged. Outside-cylinder engines, on the 'Crewe' plan, or as altered by Mr Allan and just described, were introduced as fast as the original inside-cylinder engines were worn out. The new ones had cylinders 13½ and 14 inches diameter, and 20 inches stroke; wheels, 5 feet 6 inches and 6 feet; and weighed, when charged, from 15 to 16 tons. In 1851, the standard locomotive on the same railway was substantially of similar construction to the Crewe engine; and similar engines were adopted by Mr Locke for the London and South-Western, the Paris and Rouen, the Caledonian, the Scottish Central, and other railways. On the South-Western Railway, Mr J. V. Gooch introduced, in November, 1843, an outside-cylinder engine, having 6½ feet driving-wheels, and he afterwards completed one for express trains on the same railway, having driving-wheels 7 feet in diameter, the gauge of the bine being 4 feet 8½ inches.

In April 1842, Mr R. Stephenson patented his celebrated 'long-boiler' engine. Mr Stephenson had already so well arranged the mechanism of his engine and economised space, that he found the 4 feet 8½ inches gauge afforded ample width and to spare. In lieu of the levers previously used, Mr Stephenson effected a direct communication between the excentrics and the valves, and he then proceeded to increase the power of his boiler by increasing the length of it from 8 to 12, 13, and 14 feet. If, with this length of boiler, the hind wheels had been placed, as usual, behind the fire-box, an immoderate length of bearing on the rails would have been the consequence. To obviate this, Mr Stephenson confined the bearing length of the wheels to 12 feet 9 inches between centres, his opinion being that this was the extreme length consistent with safety. In these engines, the cylinders were arranged outside the smoke-box, and placed in the same horizontal line as the centre of the driving-axle. In the year 1846, it was reported that at least 150 locomotives, according to this long-boiler pattern, were in constant use in this country and on the continental railways.

During the use of the short-boiler engines it was observed that a serious amount of destruction was going on in the 'smoke-box' and the chimney, both of which were not unfrequently red-hot, and the cylinders were sometimes split (defects which it became of the utmost importance to remove), and with a view to remedying these evils Mr Robert Stephenson caused some experiments to be made to show the amount of heat which escaped, and subsequently invented the 'long boiler'.

The experiments were made at Derby in 1843. In the first instance, *tin* was placed in small iron conical cups and suspended in the 'smoke-box', and was found to disappear quickly; next, *lead* was tried in the same manner, and was found to melt nearly as easily; and lastly, *zinc* was tried, which was soon driven off in vapour, clearly indicating a temperature 773° in the chimney, and showing that a waste of 400° at least was taking place. The 'long boiler', by its greater and more gradual distribution of the heat, was designed to remove the above serious evils, and was found so far to answer as to show a heat in the chimney very little over 442°, as upon placing *tin* as usual, it was found just to melt at the corners only, or rather to 'sweat', as it is technically termed.

Mr Stephenson found that to obtain a patent for his invention, it would be necessary to prescribe some definite arrangements of the engine, as the term 'long boiler' was unlimited in its application, and to fix a length would afford no protection, as a few inches more or less would evade the patent-right; therefore, as an arrangement necessary and consequent upon the application of a 'long boiler', the wheels were specified to be placed under the circular part of the boiler, the only suitable position, as in that day there were no turntables sufficiently large in diameter to admit of a greater distance between the axles of the wheels than was determined by the above arrangement.

The 'long-boiler' and the position of the wheels constituted Mr Stephenson's patent: but subsequently an improvement was made in it, which was to turn the cylinders over on their sides, so that their ports were opposite each other. In this position, a direct communication was effected between the excentrics and the slide-spindles.

In these 'long-boiler' engines, the driving-wheels were placed between the fore and hind carrying-wheels, the cylinders being kept forward to the outside of the smoke-box. This arrangement was found objectionable, as causing some unsteadiness at high velocities, such as 45 to 50 miles per hour; and, to avoid this, Mr Stephenson produced a new design in 1846, in which the driving-wheels were placed in the rear of the engine, and immediately in front of the fire-box, which thus overhung the wheel-bearings. This arrangement admitted of the removal of the cylinders to a position between the carrying-wheels. The most modern engines of this class have a total length of 20 feet, and length between extreme wheel-centres of 12 feet. The boiler between smoke-box and fire-box is 13 feet 6 inches long and 3 feet 6 inches diameter; the cylinders are 15 inches diameter and 24 inches stroke; driving-wheels 6 feet, and carrying-wheels 3 feet 9 inches, diameter. The outside frame is dispensed with, the axle bearings are placed inside the wheels, and the frame is simplified with a rectangular plate 1¼ inch thick and 8 inches deep.

In 1842, a class of engines of increased power was introduced on the Great Western Railway. The sample of this class, named the 'Ixion',' had inside cylinders 15¾ inches diameter and 18 inches stroke; driving-wheels 7 feet; four carrying-wheels; grate 13.4 feet; surface of fire-box 97 feet; tubes 2 inches diameter, 131 in number, surface 732 feet; total heating surface 829 feet; weight, empty, 22 tons; weight of tender, empty, 8 tons. Experiments made in December, 1845, upon this engine gave a maximum speed at the rate of 59 miles per hour with an average load of 76½ tons; and an average speed of 50 miles on a trip of 53 miles; the coke consumed was at the rate of 35.3lbs per mile, and water evaporated 201.5 feet per hour. In 1850 a yet more powerful class of engines, of which the 'Great Britain' is the type, was introduced by Messrs. Brunel and Gooch. This engine has inside cylinders, and is supported on eight wheels. The cylinders are 18 inches diameter and 24 inches stroke; surface of fire-box 153 feet; surface of grate 21 feet; tubes, 305 in number, 2 inches diameter, surface 1799 feet; total heating surface 1952 superficial feet; driving-wheels 8 feet; carrying-wheels 4 feet 6 inches diameter; weight of engine, empty, 31 tons; of tender, empty, 8½ tons; total weight, charged, 50 tons. This engine evaporates 300 cubic feet of water at high velocities; load 236 tons at 40 miles per hour, or 181 tons at 60 miles per hour. Mr Gooch considered that this class of engine was capable of evaporating 360 cubic feet of water per hour without deviating from the proper proportions of its parts.

To solve the important problem of combining a large diameter of driving-wheels with a low centre of gravity, Mr T. R. Crampton removed the driving-axle from beneath the boiler and placed it in the rear of the firebox. He then lowered the boiler as far as the axles of the carrying-wheels would permit, brought all the gearing to the outside, and increased the fire-box. In February 1843, Mr Crampton obtained a patent which included this arrangement of the driving-wheels, and in 1847 two engines were accordingly built for the Namur and Liege Railway. The first of these, named the 'Namur', was constructed with cylinders 16 inches diameter and 20 inches stroke; 182 tubes, 2 inches diameter and 11 feet long; surface of grate 14½ feet; of fire-box 62 feet; of tubes 927 feet; two driving-wheels 7 feet diameter; four carrying-wheels 3 feet 9 inches diameter; length between extreme wheel centres 13 feet. Experiments were made with this engine, before exportation, upon the London and North-Western Railway, over a total distance of 2,300 miles, and its duty was found equal to a load of 80 tons, exclusive of engine and tender, at 51 miles per hour on a level; and 50 tons at 62 miles per hour. In 1847, the first of Mr Crampton's engines for the London and Northwestern Railway was placed on that line, having cylinders 18 inches diameter and 20 inches stroke; 229 tubes, 2 inches external diameter and 12 feet long; surface of firebox 91 feet; of grate 21½ feet; of tubes 1,438 feet; total surface 1,529 feet; weight of engine, empty, 24 tons. The duty of this engine was found to equal 75 tons, besides engine and tender, at the rate of 55.4 miles per hour for a length of three miles, or 55 tons load at 53.4 miles per hour over a journey of 30 miles.

The dimensions of a trial engine built on Mr Crampton's plan, named the 'Liverpool', for the London and North-Western Railway, as a competitor on the narrow gauge, against the gigantic machines built for the broad gauge, are worth quoting :– Cylinders 18 inches diameter, 24 inches stroke; 292 tubes, $2^3/_{16}$ inches external diameter, and 8 of 1¾ inch, 12 feet 6 inches long; surface of fire-box 154.434 feet; of grate 21½ feet; of tubes 2136.117 feet; total heating surface 2,290 feet; two driving-wheels 8 feet diameter; six carrying-wheels 4 feet diameter; length between centres of extreme wheels 18 feet 6 inches; total length of engine 27 feet; weight of engine, charged, 35 tons, or 12 tons on the driving-wheels, 17 tons on the four leading wheels, and 6 tons on the two intermediate wheels; weight of tender 21 tons; total weight 56 tons. This engine conveyed the express trains between London and Wolverton for some time, and in one case took forty carriages within time, thus exceeding the combined duty of three ordinary engines. Its excessive weight and length, however, quickly threatened the stability of the permanent way, and induced its retirement from active duty, without impugning its title, however, to be regarded as the 'most powerful locomotive in the world'.

At the Great Exhibition of the Works of the Industry of all Nations, held in Hyde Park, London, in 1851, one of Mr Crampton's engines, named the 'Folkstone', was exhibited, being one of eight, built upon the same plan, by Messrs. E. Stephenson and Company, for the South-Eastern Railway. The principal features in the arrangement of these engines were described as consisting 'in the boiler resting upon three points: one on the centre of a cross spring, which bears upon the axle-boxes of the driving-wheels at the back of the fire-box, and one on each side in the front, on compensating springs, each of which springs bears upon the two axle-boxes of the small supporting wheels. The distribution of weight is for the purpose of preventing oscillation, and at the same time to insure, under all circumstances, an uniform weight upon each wheel, producing a greater amount of adhesion upon the driving-wheels with a given weight than with ordinary engines. The other principal feature consists in communicating the power from the inside cylinders to a cranked axle attached to the frame, the same as in ordinary engines, and thence by means of coupling rods to the driving-wheels behind the fire-box, the rods being arranged to act as counterweights to the inside connecting-rods, &c, the proper balancing of which is of much importance. As the crank-axle is not subjected to any blows produced by inequalities of the road or from the lateral movement of the wheels, the weight of it is reduced to one-half, and the liability to fracture from the above causes obviated. The driving-wheels being placed behind, the torsion to which the driving-axle is subjected while passing round curves is materially reduced, the cones of the wheels being properly in action, which is not the case when the driving-wheels are in the centre of the engine.' In the 'Folkstone' the boiler is 4 feet 1 inch diameter and 10 feet 8 inches in length; two driving-wheels 6 feet, and four bearing-wheels 3 feet 6 inches, in diameter. The cylinders are 15 inches diameter and 22 inches stroke; the tubes, 184 in number, are 2 inches external diameter and 11 feet long; extreme length of engine framing 24 feet; between extreme wheel centres, 16 feet. An engine of this class took 44 tons at a general speed of 65½ miles per hour, and attained a velocity at the rate of 73½ miles per hour upon a falling gradient of 1 in 264. In returning, the same engine ascended this incline with 95 tons load at the rate of 54 miles per hour.

In his 'Reports on Railway Plant', Captain Huish has shown the successive extensions which have been effected in the weights and duties of the engines and carriages, included under the general head of *Rolling Stock*. These Reports commence in 1831 on the Liverpool and Manchester Railway; and in 1837 on the Grand Junction, and London and Birmingham Railways, being the dates of their opening respectively. The Reports are brought down to the year 1848 in each case, and the extreme results may be quoted as follows:

	1831		1848	
Weights	Tons	Cwts	Tons	Cwts
Of engines, average	7	0	18	13
Of engines, greatest	7	0	37	0
Of carriages, 1st class	3	10	4	6
Of carriages, 2nd class	3	5	4	1
Of carriages, 3rd class	3	0	3	18
Of passenger trains, with engine and tender	18	0	76	0
Of goods trains, with engine and tender	52	0	160	0
Speeds				
Of goods trains, average miles per hour	10	20		
Of goods trains, greatest miles per hour	12	32		
Of passenger trains, average miles per hour	17	30		
Of passenger trains, greatest miles per hour	24	50		

As to the daily duty performed on each of these three lines, the reports show that the number of trains to and from the principal terminus of each railway respectively, viz, Manchester, Stafford, and London, during each period of twenty-four hours, had increased on the Liverpool and Manchester, from 26 in 1831, to 90 in 1848; and on the Grand Junction, from 14 in 1837, to 38 in 1848; and on the London and Birmingham, from 19 in 1837, to 44 in 1848. These few figures are quite sufficient to show how increased strength in the construction of the permanent way has become necessary, and how the requirements of each year in this essential department of railway economy have exceeded those of the preceding year.

Our notice of the locomotive apparatus of railways would not be complete if it omitted a description of the light engines constructed by Mr W. B. Adams, who advocated, with great talent and practical knowledge, the economy of reduced weight in the rolling stock of railways. The first and smallest specimen of a light engine was built by Mr Adams for Mr Samuel, then resident engineer of the Eastern Counties Railway, for the purpose of enabling him to perform his professional inspections of the line without employing special trains, or wasting his time in waiting for the ordinary trains. After some experimental constructions the engine was completed, and performed a journey to Cambridge, with eight passengers, at the rate of 25 miles per hour. The total length of the carriage is 12 feet 6 inches, including machinery, water-tank, and seats for seven passengers, all on one frame, which is hung below the axles, and is carried on four wheels 3 feet 4 inches diameter. The floor is within 9 inches of the level of the rails. The locomotive is propelled by two cylinders, 3½ inches diameter and 6 inches stroke, acting on a cranked axle. The boiler is cylindrical, placed vertically, and is 1 foot 7 inches in diameter by 4 feet 3 inches high. It contains a fire-box, 16 inches diameter by 14 inches high; with 35 tubes, 3 feet 3 inches long by 1½ inch diameter; giving 5½ feet of heating surface in the fire-box and 38 feet in the tubes. The water-tank is placed under the seat, and has a capacity for 40 gallons.

'From the weekly statement kept of the working of this engine, it appears that the number of miles run during the half-year ending 4 July 1848, was 5,526; and the quantity of coke consumed was 7 tons 9cwts, being at about the rate of 3lbs per mile. She has run altogether about 15,000 miles. The greatest speed attained on the level was 41 miles per hour. The ordinary speed that might be safely calculated upon for a long journey was 25 miles per hour. She has performed the journey from London to Cambridge, a distance of 57½ miles, in one hour and three quarters, being at the rate of nearly 33 miles per hour, with a consumption of coke 2¾lbs per mile.'

Subsequently, the carriage was christened the 'Express', went down to Birmingham to be experimented on, and ascended the Lickey incline.

'The earliest practical recogniser of the advantages offered by the light system was Mr C. H. Gregory, who advised the Directors of the Bristol and Exeter broadgauge line to order, for some of their branch traffic, a steam-carriage for first-class and second-class passengers. This was built by Mr Adams, and called the "Fair Field". The vertical boiler of the "Fair Field", though an exceedingly rapid and powerful steam-generator, was found to involve certain practical difficulties, and it was therefore replaced by a horizontal boiler.'

The following are the particulars of the construction and the performance:

'The 'Fair Field' steam-carriage was constructed for the purpose of working the Tiverton branch of the Bristol and Exeter Railway, broad gauge. It is an engine and carriage on one frame, the extreme length being 40 feet, hung on six wheels, the two front ones being drivers, 4 feet 6 inches in diameter; the middle and trailing wheels are 3 feet 6 inches in diameter. Extreme centres of wheels, 28 feet. It is propelled by two cylinders, 8 inches diameter and 12 inches stroke, acting on an independent cranked shaft, communicating by side-rods to the driving-wheels. The boiler was originally cylindrical, placed vertically, and was 6 feet in height by 3 feet diameter. The fire-box was 2 feet 6 inches diameter, with 150 tubes $1^5/_8$ inch diameter, with a heating fire-box surface of 20.6 feet, and 216 feet in the tubes. The tank is in front of the boiler, and will hold 240 gallons. The engine has since been fitted with a horizontal boiler, with a barrel 7 feet 7 inches long by 2 feet 6 inches diameter. The fire-box is 2 feet 6 inches by 2 feet 3 inches, and 4 feet in height; with 115 tubes, 8 feet long and 1½ inch diameter. The heating surface is 37 feet in the fire-box, and 325 feet in the tubes.

'The body is divided into three compartments, one first class and two second class. Passengers, total number, 58.

'The Tiverton branch is 5 miles in length, and has a rising gradient of 1 in 86.

'The maximum load taken up this gradient was, exclusive of the carriage, 31 tons 13cwts 2qrs 16lbs in 11 minutes, being at the rate of over 27 miles per hour. Eighteen trips were run, being a distance of 90 miles, during a space of 9¼ hours, the running time being about 3¾ hours, and the standing time being 5½. The consumption of coke per mile 14.8lbs. Subsequently it was reduced to 13lbs, and the engine now works with 8.7lbs.

'The load consisted of two loaded waggons, each on four wheels of 4 feet diameter; the engine and carriages on six wheels; the whole train being on fourteen wheels; while the engine and tender alone of the Great Western engines occupy fourteen wheels without any carriages.

'The "Fair Field" ran a trip from Exeter to Bristol, 76 miles – with an extra load of 10 tons behind her, equivalent to 140 passengers total – in 3 hours 37 minutes; 58 minutes being consumed in twelve stoppages, leaving the remaining time, 2 hours 39 minutes, being a fraction under 28 miles per hour. The maximum speed attained in this trip was 47 miles per hour.'

The maximum speed ultimately attained was 52 miles per hour.

'After the "Fair Field" had made considerable progress, the Directors of the Eastern Counties Railway ordered of Messrs. Adams and Co a steam-carriage, called the "Enfield", the form, proportions, and performance of which were as follow (as given by Mr Samuel, in a paper read by him at the Institution of Mechanical Engineers):

'The "Enfield" has 8-inch cylinders and 12-inch stroke; driving-wheels, 5 feet diameter; distance between centres, 20 feet; width of framing, 8 feet 6 inches. The boiler is of the ordinary locomotive construction, 5 feet long by 2 feet 6 inches diameter. The fire-box is 2 feet 10½ inches by 2 feet 6 inches.

'There are 115 tubes of 1½ inch diameter, and 5 feet 3 inches in length, giving a total of 230 feet heating surface in the tube. The area of the fire-box is 25 feet, giving a total heating surface of 255 feet.

'The weight of this steam-carriage is 15 tons 7cwts in working trim. The engine and carriage being combined, it is evident that the weight on the driving-wheels is increased by the load carried, and that this weight increases in the same ratio as the load required to be taken.

'The extreme distance between the centres of the leading and trailing wheels being 20 feet, accounts for the steadiness of this machine; there is, indeed, no perceptible oscillation when travelling at the highest speed; and this verifies the observation "that the steadiness of an engine depends not on the position of the driving-wheel, but upon the length of the rectangle covered by the wheels". This engine at the same time daily traverses curves of 5 or 6 chains radius.

'The "Enfield" steam-carriage was originally intended to convey 84 passengers; but as it was found that when she was put on as an express-train the passengers increased in number, a "North Woolwich" carriage was attached capable of conveying 116 passengers, and also a guard's break-van, making provision altogether for 150 passengers, which is now her regular train taken at a speed of 37 miles per hour.

'The following return shows the miles run and coke consumed by this engine, during the 7½ months regular working from January 29th to September 9th, 1849:

14,021 total miles run.
   705 hours, running time.
_1,457 ditto, standing time.
_2,162 total hours in steam.

   743 cwts coke consumed in running.
   408 cwts coke consumed in standing.
  _286 cwts coke consumed in getting up steam.
_1,437 cwts total coke consumed.
11 48lbs per mile average consumption of coke.

'The "Enfield" is in steam 15 hours per day, the fire being lighted about six in the morning and drawn at ten o'clock at night. But, of

these 15 hours, it appears, by the return, that she is engaged running
only 5 hours, the remaining 10 being employed standing in the siding.
It was found by experiment, that the quantity of coke consumed
standing was 32lbs per hour; and, after deducting this and the quantity
consumed getting up steam, it will appear that the actual consumption
of coke running is under 6lbs per mile.

'It must also be particularly borne in mind that this consumption of
coke includes the total goods and coal traffic on the branch, amounting
to 1,410 tons, viz. 169 tons of goods and 1,241 tons of coal.

'The "Enfield" steam-carriage worked the ten a.m. passenger train
from London to Ely, on 14 June, a distance of 72 miles, taking behind
her three of the ordinary carriages and two horse-boxes; she arrived
at Ely eight minutes before time, and the total consumption of fuel,
including the getting-up steam, was found to be 8¾lbs per mile. The
tubes of the boiler are only 5 feet 3 inches in length, and the economy
of fuel is consequently scarcely at the maximum.'

Expansion Gear

Up to the year 1838, or thereabouts, the mechanism of the valves of
locomotive engines does not appear to have been designed with any
view of altering the *rate of expansion* of the steam within the cylinders.
The action of the valves, and the expansion they permitted, as used in
1838, have been already fully described. In or about 1839, it was found
desirable to *vary* the rate of expansion at different parts of the stroke,
and a form of gearing for effecting this is reported to have been first
applied by Mr John Gray to a locomotive engine on the Liverpool and
Manchester Railway.

The overlap of $1/16$ inch in the valves has been already described, and the
use of it explained in describing Fig. 9. The amount of *overlap*, or '*lap*',
as it is more familiarly called, determined, of course, the extent to which
expansion of the steam was permitted, the expansion being understood
to be an action of the steam within the cylinder *after* the steam has ceased
to arrive, and before it has begun to depart. The lap of $1/16$ inch only left
little time for exhausting the steam previous to the commencement of the
return stroke, and the necessary rapidity of the alternate strokes increased
the evil effects of this imperfect exhaustion. By successive improvements
in increasing the lap to 1 inch, the gross average consumption of coke
per mile was reduced from 49lbs to 28lbs; and further improvements
applied to new engines with enlarged exhausting passages, larger tubes,
closer fire-bars, and superior construction, still reduced the consumption
from 28lbs to 15lbs per mile, as appeared from the experience upon
the Liverpool and Manchester Railway during the years from 1839 to

1844, reported by Mr E. Woods. The economical value of the *increased lap* having been appreciated, the succeeding desideratum, which almost naturally followed it, was such an arrangement of gearing as would permit the rapidity of the passage of the steam to be regulated by the position of the piston, or part of the stroke; in other words, an arrangement which would provide for a *varying expansion* of the steam. Mr Gray's gearing for this purpose has been already mentioned. This was further developed by Mr Williams, and introduced with such improvements as made it not only practicable, but deserving of retention since its introduction by Mr Howe and Messrs. Stephenson in 1843. In this gearing, the ends of the excentric-rods are connected by a curved *link,* in the opening or *slot* of which a *sliding*-block, attached to the end of the *slide valve-rod,* is movable. The ends of the excentric-rods and the link may be moved vertically, and supported at any required elevation. The nearer that the centre of the link approaches the sliding-block, the shorter is the *travel* or stroke of the valve, and of course the greater is the amount of expansion.

Part II

The Modern Locomotive

By D. K. Clark, M. Inst. C.E.

Section I: General Description

Chapter 1

Introduction

It is hardly necessary to observe that a locomotive engine differs in many particulars from other steam-engines. The source of power – heat in steam – is a point of agreement; it determines the order to which the locomotive naturally belongs. But in this we have a new species, adapted to other purposes, and possessing different capabilities. The machine, as its name imports, is intended for locomotion; and, in order that it may fulfil its purpose, it must carry along with it the fuel and water which are necessary to maintain its action. This condition implies compactness and lightness of construction, combined with the requisite power. For the attainment of these objects the engine and the boiler are placed together in the same machine, and the parts are made of much smaller dimensions in proportion to the power than in other steam-engines. The requisite power is obtained by using steam of very high pressure – of such a pressure as will allow the steam-cylinders, when the power is developed, to be of small capacity; but in order to obtain steam in sufficient quantity, and of sufficient pressure, from a boiler which must also be portable, it was necessary to depart from the common form, and to adopt a mode of construction by which the evaporative power of the boiler – that is, its power of generating steam – would be greatly augmented. The condition of locomotion at high velocity in so weighty a mass, as even the lightest and most compact locomotive must be, implies, moreover, subjection to violent strains and shocks, which must, as far as possible, be provided against by strength and firmness in the framing together of the whole.

The 'Rocket', famous in history, comprised the three elements of efficiency of the modern locomotive: there was, first, the internal water-surrounded fire-box and the multitubular flue in the boiler, being a number of small tubes in place of one large tube; secondly, the blast-pipe, from which the waste steam of the engine was exhausted up the chimney; and the direct connection of the steam-cylinders, two in number, one on each side of the engine, with the driving or propelling wheels on one axle. The envelopment of the fire in an enclosure of water, together with subdivision of the flue into a number of small tubes, proved to be of marvellous advantage in accelerating the absorption of heat by the water and the generation of steam, in virtue of the great increase of heated surface applied to the water, without adding to the size or the weight of the boiler. But the evaporating tubes would not have been of much avail practically had they not been supplemented by the blast-pipe in the chimney, which, by ejecting the steam from the engine after it had done its work in the cylinder, straight up the chimney, excited a strong draught through the boiler, and caused a brisk and rapid combustion of fuel and generation of heat. The heat was absorbed with proportional rapidity through the newly applied heating tubes. By the agency of the blast-pipe, in conjunction with the multitubular flue, the range and capacity of the locomotive were vastly augmented; and in further conjunction with the direct connection of the steam-cylinders to one axle and pair of wheels, the locomotive, in the hands of Stephenson, became a new and original machine.

In the modern locomotive, the results of a lengthened and improving experience have demonstrated the practical advantages of clearly distinguishing the three functional departments of the machine – constructively as well as speculatively – showing that the systems embodying these departments, whilst they should be consecutive, and should together form a complete unity, should also be, as much as may be, self-contained. The three particular systems are – the *boiler,* the *engine,* and the *carriage.* The function of the boiler is to generate the power; that of the engine is to convert the power into tractive force; and that of the carriage is to apply the tractive force to the train. The last of these – the carriage, embracing a consideration of the frame and the wheels, and of the conditions of stability in working and in running – is that section of the locomotive to which attention shall first be directed.

Chapter 2

The Frame and the Wheels

The functions of the frame of the locomotive are to fulfil the duty of a foundation for the boiler and the engine proper; to carry the wheels and axles; to serve as the medium of communication between the cylinder and the driving-wheels, and between the driving-wheels and the train. The first great defect in the design of locomotives, and the last to have been acknowledged, was the employment of the boiler as a foundation for the engine, or as a means of communication between the cylinders and the driving-axle. When the cylinders were fixed upon the smoke-box, within or without it, and sustained by it, the direct stress due to the steam-pressure on the pistons was transmitted to the driving-axle, either through the tube-plate and the barrel of the boiler, or still more circuitously through the lateral connections of the smoke-box with the frame. Moreover, it was a common practice to pull the train from the back of the fire-box, where an attachment was made for the draw-bar. Here was an additional complication; for the stress originated by the pressure of steam on the smoke-box at the fore end of the boiler was first led to the frame outside, and then returned to the fire-box at the hind end of the boiler. The practical effect was that the boilers were sprung in the neighbourhoods of the places where the stresses were applied, leakages were started, and the circuitous action became a permanent source of trouble and annoyance.

It was, of course, found necessary, while this vicious system of construction was practised, to strengthen the boiler – in fact, to adapt it to the extra duty imposed upon it. In some instances, a large and heavy angle-iron was laid into the angle of the barrel and the smoke-box, underneath the barrel, to act as a strengthening knee; in others, the angle-iron employed to unite the barrel to the smoke-box was of an extra size all the way round the lower semi-circumference of the barrel, fixed with an accumulation of double-riveting. Then, again, other makers, sceptical of the efficiency of the indirect strengthening, applied binding plates directly between the smoke-box and the fire-box shell, joining them by rivets and bolts and nuts. But this appliance introduced another evil of a totally different origin, arising from the variable length of the barrel of the boiler, and the consequently varying distance apart of the smoke-box and fire-box, due to the expansion and contraction of the boiler by alternate heating and cooling. The binding plates, necessarily, either pulled the boiler together as it expanded, and thereby strained the seams, or they loosened their hold of the boiler plates, and became in so far useless. Another expedient consisted in thickening the plates in the lower half of the barrel to meet the exigencies of the extra duty.

The ultimate solution of the problem was effected in the simplest possible way, *by detaching the cylinders from the smoke-box as a fulcrum, and uniting them directly to the framing.* No doubt, incidentally, the smoke-box plates might be fitted and bolted to the cylinder-ends, but not, as previously, for any purpose of deriving support from the boiler. They are united because it is convenient that they should be united, and because it is desirable, and indeed necessary, to form an air-tight smoke-box; and, further, because in so far as the cylinders are bolted together into one firm mass, and firmly embrace the side frame-plates, they are identified with the frame, and constitute part of it.

For illustration, the Figs. 25 are annexed,[2] showing the comparative practice of early constructors. Nos. 1 and 3 are examples of the original compound-framed engine, in which the axle-bearings were outside the wheels, and the driving-axle had auxiliary bearings inside; as the latter bearings gave way by wear, and the axle depended upon the outer bearings alone, it obviously became liable to very unfair straining from the transverse action of the steam-pressure through the connecting-rods. The drawbar was coupled to the frame of No. 1, and to the fire-box of No. 3, in the latter of which it is plain that, when the inside bearings wore slack, the labour of traction devolved chiefly upon the outside frame, and acted through the brackets upon the boiler, from which it passed off to the drawbar. Thus, whilst the brackets in No. 1 were strained and shaken loose at the outset, and so long as the inside bearings were in good condition, in transmitting the tractive stress to the outside frame, those in No. 3 were overstrained and loosened only after the inside bearings fell into disorder. In so far, the second was an improvement on the first; but either way, the evil of indirect connection became manifest by experience.

In No. 2, by Bury, the framing and the axle-bearings were exclusively inside, and the draw-centre was sustained by the frame, quite clear of the boiler. Thus all the action was confined between the wheels, and the driving-axle was supported close to the cranks, much to the advantage of the axle.

No. 4 shows the design of framing adopted by Sharp, previous to and about the year 1855. The frame-beams are carried up to the buffer-

---

2. Borrowed from *Railway Machinery,* diagram-plate 7.

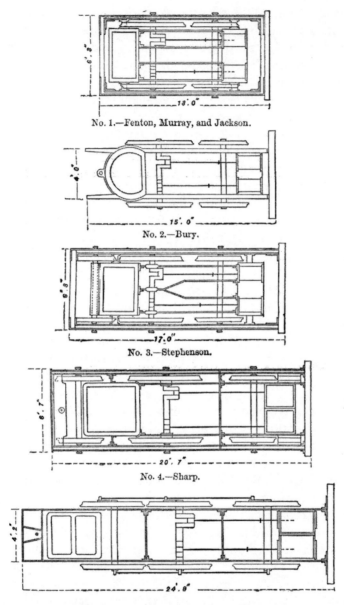

No. 1.—Fenton, Murray, and Jackson.

No. 2.—Bury.

No. 3.—Stephenson.

No. 4.—Sharp.

Figure 25. Examples of Locomotive Framing.

beam, and bolted to it; they are also bound together by a transverse plate, employed to sustain portions of the valve-gear, and by the cylinder-castings, with plating riveted with angle-iron. The inside frame-plates terminate at the fire-box, and the outside framing is bound together behind the fire-box with plates to which the draw-bolt is attached. The driving-axle has four large bearings, inside as well as outside. This style of framing is rigid, in its way; yet even such an accumulation of plates and rivets would break loose from its fixings to the inside frame-plates and to the boiler, by reason of the horizontal wear of the inside axle-boxes, their desertion from duty, and the inevitable concentration of the steam-pressure upon the outside bearings.

No. 5, by Sharp, exemplifies an excellent design of framing for a goods engine. The frame is strictly self-contained, simple, and direct; it receives and transmits all the straining within itself, from the cylinders fastened to it at the fore end, to the draw-bar attached to the draw-plate, which is riveted to it at the hind end.

Stability of the Locomotive as a Carriage

It has already been shown that all locomotives, excepting, it may be, such as may be specially designed for siding and shunting work, at low speeds, should be carried by six wheels with three axles at least, so disposed that one pair of wheels is placed behind the boiler, and the other two pairs under the barrel of the boiler, of which one pair is just in front of the fire-box and the other pair is just behind the cylinders. This is the arrangement of the normal locomotive of Stephenson, Fig. 4, page 14; and it is apparent that the construction of a locomotive-boiler lends itself so readily to such an arrangement of wheels and axles, that no other principle of arrangement has ever come into favour since the Stephenson six-wheel engine was first brought out. The reasons which led to this uniformity of practice are not difficult of appreciation. In the first place, there is the demand for a sufficient amount of driving weight to supply the required adhesion for traction; but the apportioning of driving weight to one pair of wheels must be executed with a regard to the requirements of the others, which are carrying-wheels simply. The function of the front wheels is to lead the engine, and that of the hind wheels, as carriers, is mainly to steady it. Thus the front wheels require a greater load than the hind wheels, but not so much as the drivers; and the drivers stand first, the leaders next, and the trailers last in the order of loading. It naturally follows that, for the driving-wheels of single engines, the best situation is near to the centre of gravity of the whole machine, where the desired amount of loading may be applied without materially affecting the relation of the loads at the leading and the trailing wheels, as between themselves.

Chapter 3

Conditions of Stability

That a six-wheeled engine thus disposed may run with steadiness, supposing, of course, that the engine is otherwise well constructed, the one primary and sufficient condition is that the revolving and reciprocating masses of the pistons, piston-rods, crossheads, connecting-rods, and cranks, should be balanced in the wheels. This condition was pointed out many years ago by Mr Robert Stephenson, in his evidence before the Gauge Commissioners, in 1845; and he at the same time exposed the fallacy that the action of the steam on the pistons had anything necessarily to do with unsteadiness. 'When the steam presses upon the piston,' he says, 'it at the same time presses against the lid of the cylinder; the action and reaction must be equal. Therefore, I do not believe that it is the steam that causes the irregular action, but I believe it to be the mere weight of the pistons themselves; and if we could contrive to balance the pistons by the weight upon the wheel, we should get rid of that very much.' All classes of engines, with inside or with outside cylinders, with single or with coupled wheels, may be satisfactorily balanced on the principle above indicated.

Economy of fuel is materially promoted by the correct equilibration of engines. The writer, in 1856, balanced, by means of counterweights in the wheels, the 'Canute' engine on the London and South-Western Railway. This engine had previously a balance-weight of 85lbs applied within the rims of the driving-wheels. New weights were put in, weighing 186lbs for each wheel, and balancing the whole mass acting at the crank-pin. The engine ran so much more steadily and freely with the new balance-weights as to take the engineman by surprise. On the first day after the alteration, the stations were considerably overshot by the engine, although the steam was shut-off and the brakes applied at the usual distance from the stations. The saving in fuel by the improvement in the counter-weighting of the engine was estimated at 20 per cent.

M. Le Chatelier has fully demonstrated the beneficial results of correctly equilibrating locomotive engines. He found that an engine unbalanced could not attain so high a speed as when balanced. He worked a six-coupled goods-engine with outside inclined cylinders, and 4 feet 3 inch wheels. This class of engine had been found very unsteady on the rails, and had required frequent repairs. Counter-weights, equivalent to 1,100lbs at the crank-pin, were equally distributed between the three wheels on each side of the engine, well worn by long service. They were placed exactly opposite the cranks, the total weight being less than would have exactly balanced the engine. With a train of 44 waggons, at 30 miles per hour, the engine ran with steadiness, though the wheels had already been well worn, and the axle-boxes had acquired a considerable amount of play. The counter-weights having then been removed, the engine was again set to work with the same train, when it was found impossible to attain a higher speed than 25 miles per hour, as the engine ran very unsteadily – being affected with violent oscillation and fore-and-aft movement. The economy of fuel effected by the equilibration of this locomotive is testified to by the results of the performance of this engine before and after having been equilibrated:

January, 1849 – 50.3lbs of coke per mile, without counter-weights.
February, 1849 – 42.3lbs of coke per mile, average of 12 trips, of which 10 trips only were made with counterweights.

Here there is a saving of 8lbs per mile, or 16 per cent.

The operation of the reciprocating parts of the mechanism as disturbing causes, tending to excite angular or pendulous movements, horizontally and vertically, and also longitudinal fore-and-aft movements, is readily explained. The reciprocating parts are, during each stroke, started from a state of rest with accelerated motion, which attains to its maximum at half-stroke; during the second half of the stroke they are retarded in motion, and finally brought to a state of rest at the end of the stroke. Such proportion of the pressure of the steam in the cylinders as is necessary to impress upon the pistons and other reciprocating parts the accelerated movement, is necessarily exerted upon the cylinder-cover – acting as a spring as between the cover and the reciprocating parts – and, through the cylinder, upon the body of the engine. The whole machine, therefore, supposing that there is no counterbalance-weight, is swayed to one side. During the second half of the stroke, on the contrary, the momentum acquired by the reciprocating parts is delivered to the crank-pin and the axle, and thence to the whole machine; thus it is caused to sway horizontally in the contrary direction. This double action is repeated during the return-stroke of the piston, and thus it follows that the engine is subjected to four distinct and contrary swerving impulses during one revolution of each crank, or eight impulses in all, reckoning for two cylinders, during one revolution of the driving-wheels.

When the engine runs without steam, the circumstances under which the accelerated movement of the pistons is acquired are different from those which exist when the engine is running with steam on the pistons. In the absence of steam on the pistons, the labour of starting and of accelerating the motion of the piston devolves upon the crank on the driving-axle; so that the swaying stress is transferred from the end of the machine, where the cylinder is placed, to the middle. This change of circumstances, though it does not affect the longitudinal reciprocating movement, increases the lateral oscillation, because the disturbing force has, in the latter case, more power over the mass of the machine.

With respect to disturbance arising from the action of the steam on the pistons, apart from that which is absorbed in accelerating them, the angularity of the connecting-rod gives rise to an upward pressure upon the guide-bars when the engine is going ahead, tending to lift the engine off its leading springs at half-stroke. The alternate heaving and sinking so caused is called the *pitching* of the engine; and, further, as the upward movement is not simultaneous for the two cylinders, but successive, the heaving of the engine takes place alternately on the two sides, and causes a rocking, or laterally rolling motion on the springs.

There is another source of unsteadiness in the unequal quantities of steam admitted to the two ends of the cylinder, with imperfectly arranged valve-gear, by which a greater quantity of steam is admitted into the cylinder, and a greater mean pressure is reached during the front stroke of the piston than during the back stroke. As the two front strokes of the two pistons take place consecutively in the course of a revolution of the driving-wheels, and alternately with the two back strokes of the two pistons, together, it follows that a varying impulsive force must be exerted upon the engine, resulting in a longitudinal reciprocating movement of the whole machine when in motion.

Practically, it is found that, for engines with inside cylinders, counterweights in the wheels, equivalent to three-fourths of the gross disturbing weight on each side of the engine, is sufficient to insure the external stability of the engine on the rails. For engines with outside cylinders, the counterweights should be equivalent to the whole disturbing weights; or, at least for single engines, not less than seven-eighths of the weight. The balance-weight should be distributed over at least two or three spaces, or intervals, between the spokes of the wheels, to distribute and reduce the unequal wear of the tyres by vertical action, and the tendency to slip at high speed.

Chapter 4

The Boiler

'In the fire-box and the boiler,' says Pambour, 'resides the real source of the effects of the engine'; and a few remarks may now be made on the mechanical principles on which the action of this admirable steam-generator is based. In the fire-box and the tubes the heat is generated and conducted, which is destined for the generation of steam; and this is effected by the passage of the heat through the material of the fire-box and the tubes, and the absorption of the heat by the water with which these are everywhere surrounded. The surface thus presented for the transmission of heat is known as *heating surface*. The efficiency of this surface – rather its opportunity for transmitting heat – depends very much on the situation of it. Mr Armstrong found that a cubical metallic box submerged in water, and heated from within, generated steam from its upper surface more than twice as fast, per unit of area, as it did from the sides when they were held in a vertical position, and that the bottom yielded none at all. These remarkable differences arose out of the difficulty with which steam separates from a vertical surface on which it is formed, to give place to fresh charges of water, and to the impossibility of its leaving the inverted surface at all. By slightly inclining the box, the elevated side parted much more easily with the steam, and the rate of evaporation was increased; whilst, on the depressed side, the steam hung so sluggishly as to lead to an over-heating of the metal. It is, therefore, clearly of importance to incline inwardly the walls of the fire-box; the more so as they are closely hedged in by the outer shell, which leaves but a thin wall of water in contact with them, and thus restricts the circulation both of water and of steam. In early practice, with comparatively small fire-boxes, water-spaces 4 or 5 inches wide were made, which were, no doubt, better for circulation than the 2½-inch or 3-inch spaces which are now allowed. In a number of Bury's circular fire-boxes, of which the outer shells were flattened externally to make room for the frame-bars, the prevailing water-space, only 2½ inches, was reduced, in construction, to 2 inches at those places. 'Nature' rebelled; the rising steam became entangled, the fire-boxes were bulged inwards about half an inch by the pressure on the over-heated plate, just opposite the flattened outer part, and restored the narrowed water space to the regular width of 2½ inches.

That sufficient space is required to ensure a sufficient degree of free circulation for the steam and the water, amongst and around the flue-tubes, has been amply proved by the results of experience. In many cases, the tubes have been placed so near to each other as to retard injuriously the circulation and the escape of steam, and consequently also the generation of fresh steam. A notable instance of the overcrowding of flue-tubes is found in the large eight-wheel locomotives of the 'Great Britain' class, constructed more than thirty years ago for the Great Western Railway. The facilities afforded by the broad gauge (7 feet) for augmenting the size of the boiler were realised in the design of those engines. They were constructed with 305 flue-tubes, placed at clear distances of ½ inch only apart; and they were, moreover, packed so closely to the sides of the barrel of the boiler, which was 4 feet 8 inches in diameter, as to hinder the circulation exteriorly to the tubes. In contrast with this boiler may be noted the section of the boiler and tubes of the 'Sphynx' goods engine, constructed by Messrs. Sharp Brothers and Co If less ambitiously designed, the boiler was much more effective. The barrel of the 'Sphynx" was only 3 feet 8 inches in diameter, being 1 foot less than that of the 'Great Britain', and it contained 142 tubes, $2^1/_8$ inches in diameter, placed at about $^9/_{16}$ inch clear apart. Thus the 'Sphynx' had less than half as many tubes as the 'Great Britain', and they were actually more widely apart, whilst there was a considerable width of free space for circulation at the sides of the barrel. What was the result? That equal quantities of water were evaporated per hour by the two kinds of boiler – namely, 233 cubic feet per hour; and that the 'Sphynx' did the work with a consumption of 1,663lbs of coke per hour; whilst in the 'Great Britain' 1,891lbs of coke were consumed per hour for equal evaporative duties. Here, it is clearly evidenced that the expedient of increasing the number of tubes, by packing them more closely together, resulted in failure, since less than half the augmented number did equal duty with a less consumption of fuel. The fire-box of the 'Sphynx', too, was only about half the size of that of the 'Great Britain'. So that it may, in general terms, be affirmed that the 'Great Britain', having in all respects double the nominal capacity of boiler of the 'Sphynx', did not do any more evaporative work, and consumed more fuel for the duty.

The relative working efficiencies of the fire-box and the flue-tubes of locomotive-boilers has been a subject of much discussion. The question, nevertheless, is simple. The surface of the fire-box is by far the more efficient in evaporative duty; for the reason that, being 'within sight of the fire', it receives the direct heat radiated from the incandescent fuel, whilst the surface of the tubes is necessarily deprived of radiant heat. Again, the surface of the fire-box is exposed to the heat carried in the burnt gases which rise from the fuel, when the gases are at their maximum temperature. Obviously, therefore, the fire-box heating surface is by far more active for the absorption and transmission of heat and the evaporation of water than the surface of the flue-tubes. Mr Robert Stephenson had early recognised the essentially different conditions under which the fire-box and the tubes performed their functions of absorption and evaporation. He constructed a box, similar to the fire-box of the 'Rocket' engine, surrounded by a water-space casing, open at the top, having 6 square feet of direct heating surface. A separate chest, 5½ feet long and 16 inches wide, was attached to the fire-box, traversed by nine 3-inch tubes, placed in communication with the fire-box, exposing a surface of 40½ square feet. But, whilst the tube-surface amounted to more than eight times the fire-box surface, it only evaporated one-third more water in the same time than was done by the fire-box surface; insomuch that whilst, by each square foot of fire-box surface, 16lbs of water was evaporated per hour, the water evaporated by one square foot of tube-surface only amounted to 3lbs. Here the tube-surface performed, in proportion, less than a fifth part of the work of evaporation done by the fire-box surface.

The results of experiments made, with a similar object, upon locomotive-boilers of modern construction, develop, in a still more striking manner, the remarkable inequality of performance of the heating surface of such boilers. Mr Edward Woods and Mr John Dewrance, testing the evaporative duty of successive portions of the flue-tubes of a locomotive-boiler, in which the tubes were 5 feet 6 inches long, the tubes were divided into six compartments by vertical diaphragms, of which the first compartment was 6 inches long, and the others were each 12 inches long. It was found that the evaporative duty of the first compartment was about the some per square foot as that of the fire-box; that of the second compartment about a third of that value; that of the remaining compartments very small; and that the first 6 inches did more work than the remaining 60 inches of tubes.

Much more evidence to the same effect, that much the greater proportion of the evaporative work is done in and near the locality of the furnace, might be adduced; and Mr Gooch, now Sir Daniel Gooch, spoke not without reason, when he maintained that the evaporative power of the locomotive-boiler depended very much upon the extent of the fire-box surface; and that the evaporative duty of the boiler followed approximately the rate of 2 cubic feet of water per square foot of fire-box surface per hour. This, it is manifest, cannot be recognised as a general principle, though it may be useful empirically.

Chapter 5

Coal-Burning Boilers

The locomotive-boiler, though it was designed originally for the combustion of coke as fuel, has been, with a great degree of success, adapted for the combustion of coal, now universally used as fuel on railways. The physical conditions of the combustion of coal are, first, that air should be introduced into the fire-box in sufficient quantity, and should be suitably distributed amongst the solid and the gaseous portions of the fuel in the furnace, altogether, or partially through the grate and partially above the fuel, directly to the gases; secondly, that the temperature should be maintained sufficiently high within the furnace, so that it should not be lowered by external causes during the combustion of the hydro-carbon gases, in order to effect the union of the element of carbon with its full proportion of oxygen; and, thirdly, that the combustible gases should be thoroughly mixed with their supply of air.

With the comparatively limited fire-box of a common locomotive-boiler, in its normal form, to deal with, engine-men had recourse to various ways of treating the fire in order to diminish the nuisance of smoke. They relied chiefly on the instrumentality of the ashpan, the dampers, and the fire-door for carrying out a system of careful firing. They endeavoured to prevent the formation of smoke by curtailing the admission of air through the grate, and adjusting the supply precisely to the requirements of the fuel by similarly manoeuvring the fire-door for the admission of air above the fuel; by stoking with large pieces of coal and deep fires for heavy duty, and smaller coal with shallow fires for lighter duty; by firing frequently, to lighten the duty; and, at all times, by keeping the bars covered with fuel, to prevent excessive local draughts through the grate.

Certainly, much was effected by these means. It is well understood that the nuisance of smoke, on entering or in waiting at stations, was very much, or in some cases even altogether, subdued by thoroughly closing the ashpan and opening wide the fire-door. By low-pitched doorways, at the level of the fuel, fresh air was introduced to greater advantage than by such doorways as were pitched high; for the air which passed by the low doorway mixed more quickly and more freely with the combustible gases as they rose. It was accordingly found advantageous to adopt the practice of charging the fresh coal chiefly under the fire-door, upon the hinder part of the grate; and, subsequently, when it was relieved of its gaseous elements, pushing it forward towards the tube-plate; thus making way for a fresh charge of coal behind it. Such were the usual modes of treating coal, as fuel, in locomotive-boilers of the normal type, in their normal condition. But the elaborations of practice in the stoking of ordinary boilers – stoking under difficulties – were superseded to a considerable extent by special methods of admitting air above the fuel, near its surface, and amongst the combustible gases. These methods may be classed as acting; first, by currents of air introduced through tubular or other openings in the sides of the fire-box, uniformly distributed over the surface of the fuel; and, secondly, by the deflection of a body of air, introduced through the doorway, upon and over the surface of the fuel. A different principle of operation has also been introduced by constructing large and spacious fire-boxes with large grates and long runs.

Of the three classes of coal-burning boilers thus indicated, the last-named was the first in chronological order, comprising the adaptation of large extended fire-boxes and combustion-chambers by Mr J. E. M'Connell, in 1853; by Mr Joseph Beattie, in 1855; and by Mr J. J. Cudworth, in 1857.

But it was necessary to adapt existing engines, as they were, for burning coal without smoke by simple means, and independently of extensive structural alterations. Such adaptation had been attempted by Messrs. Gray and Chanter, in 1837, and again in 1839, on the Liverpool and Manchester Railway. They divided the fire-box into two compartments – one for coal, the other for coke; they also admitted air in streams through tubes in the walls of the fire-box; and they were the first who applied a jet of steam in the chimney, when the blast was off, to maintain a draught. The half-burned products of combustion from the coal-fire were passed through the coke-fire, to be reheated and completely consumed – a system which, if it had been strictly accomplished, would only have ended in extinguishing the coke-fire. Mr Samuel Hall, about the year 1841, applied to locomotives on the Midland Railway a system of introducing air by tubes through the walls of the fire-box, immediately above the surface of the fire; and by extensions of some of the flue-tubes of the boiler through the smoke-box, to the front, expanded into bell-mouths, to collect air and conduct it through the boiler into the fire-place. Mr John Dewrance, in 1845, on the Liverpool and Manchester Railway, divided the fire-box into two parts – the furnace and the combustion-chamber. Messrs. Dubs and Douglas, in 1856, constructed a deflecting mid-feather or water-partition, proceeding from the back of the fire-box towards the tube-plate, to throw down the smoke over the incandescent fuel; and Messrs. Evans and Dubs, in 1857, added to this a movable inclined grate, capable of being raised or lowered for the management of the fire. After various attempts, Mr Thomas Yarrow, in 1857, projected an arch of firebrick from the tube-plate towards the fire-door, and admitted air through tubes in the tube-plate, under the arch and through the fire-door, to mix with the combustible gases. Subsequently, he superseded the air-tubes by upright air-bars near the tube-plate. In the same year, Mr Jenkins, admitting air through numerous air-tubes in the tube-plate, applied a curved partition or baffler across the fire-box, to throw forward the air, distributing it through numerous small holes at the upper part. He regulated the supply of air by a damper, and afterwards he added a row of air-tubes under the fire-door.

Towards the end of 1857, the writer, believing that a simple means of increasing the supply of air, and forcibly distributing and mixing it with the combustible gases in a common open fire-box, independently of internal appliances, was a desideratum, devised his system of steam-inducted air-currents, which was patented on 30 November 1857. In this system, in its simplest form, air-currents are admitted just above the fuel, by tubes through the walls of the fire-box, and are forcibly accelerated by means of jets of steam directed from the outside through the openings into and across the fire-box, the steam-nozzles operating in the air-tubes as the blast does in the chimney. In December 1857, the writer applied his system to a small stationary locomotive-boiler at the Railway Foundry, New Cross. There were two air-tubes, and a jet of steam to each tube from small nozzles on the outside, $1/16$ inch in diameter, to increase the quantity and velocity of the air introduced. This simple apparatus was in operation for several months, and the dark smoke which was frequently discharged when it was not in action, was entirely prevented by its use. In January 1858, a tank-engine on the North London Railway was fitted with four air-tubes, 1½ inch in diameter, through one side only, the other side having been inaccessible. With the assistance of $1/16$-inch jets of steam, smoke was completely prevented when the surface of the fuel was below the level of the air-tubes. In April 1858, a passenger-engine, No. 64, on the Eastern Counties Railway, was fitted with a row of air-tubes on each side – four on one side and three on the other side – with steam-nozzles, one to each air-tube. With this appliance, the engine worked the main-line trains for eight or nine months, and the smoke was in general effectually prevented. In January 1859, a passenger-engine on the South-Eastern Railway was fitted and put to work with two rows of air-tubes, one through the front wall and one through the back wall of the fire-box – seven tubes in each row, or fourteen tubes in all – with an induction steam-nozzle to each tube. On the Great North of Scotland Railway an engine was fitted on the writer's system, with front and back air-tubes, under the direction of Mr William Cowan, the locomotive engineer of the line, and it was started in March 1859. The results were in all respects satisfactory, and the same system has been applied by Mr Cowan to the entire locomotive stock of that railway. In 1859 one of the old passenger-engines of the London, Brighton, and South Coast Railway was fitted with the writer's apparatus, having a row of air-tubes and induction-jets in the front only. Accidental circumstances rendered impracticable the insertion of air-tubes in the back. Smoke was effectually prevented, except when heavy charges of coal were delivered at once. On the Great Western Railway coal-smoke has been prevented by admitting air in the fire-box over the fuel through numerous air-tubes in the front, sides, and back. On the Oxford, Worcester, and Wolverhampton Railway a system was introduced by Mr Edward Wilson, in 1858, in which air was conducted from the front of the smoke-box through several of the lower flue-tubes into the fire-box, reminding one of the experiments previously made by Mr Hall. On the Northern Division of the London and North-Western Railway, Mr John Ramsbottom, in 1859, introduced air under a brick arch by two openings, 7 inches square, through the front of the fire-box; governed, of course, by dampers.

With respect to the class of contrivances acting by deflection, the initiative appears to have been taken on the Birkenhead Railway, by Mr Douglas, who, in January 1858, applied a deflecting-plate, fixed to the inner side of the doors, through openings in which air was admitted, whence the air passed and was deflected towards the fuel. In June 1858, on the same line, a movable deflecting-plate and an underhung door, with a sector, and notches to regulate the opening for air, was applied; and, more recently, a plain inverted scoop or shovel. In July 1858, on the East Lancashire Railway, Messrs. Lees and Jacques fixed the deflector to the door, which was underhung and was provided with a valve, the opening of which was regulated by a sector. They built, in addition, a narrow brick arch against the tube-plate, so that the smoke and air might, by the combined action of the arch and the door, be better intermixed. In December 1858, Mr Robert Sinclair, on the Eastern Counties Railway, applied a baffle-plate inside the fire-box, hung over the doorway, and an underhung door, regulated by notches, with two steam-roses, one on each side of the fire-box, to propel steam downwards upon the fuel when the blast was off. This system was the invention of Mr Frodsham, following chronologically the trial of the writer's system on the same railway, in which steam had been successfully employed for completing the intermixture of the elements.

In 1858–59 an inverted shovel or scoop, similar to Mr Douglas's, but larger, was, and has since been, extensively introduced, being placed in the doorway, and inclined towards the centre of the fire, in order to deliver the air directly on the top of the fuel.

In 1858–60 the Midland Railway Company made many experiments on the burning of coal in locomotives. They introduced a brick arch into the smoke-box, in connection with a long deflecting-plate from the doorway, and sliding doors on the outside of the fire-box, consisting of two half door-plates connected to slide simultaneously towards each other or apart, and thus to regulate the supply of air through the doorway. Mr Charles Markham[3] stated that he obtained the most satisfactory results with a deflector-plate 3 feet in length, and a doorway 18 inches by 11 inches, for a grate 14 square feet in area. The area of this doorway was 1.1 square foot, being at the rate of 11.3 square inches per square foot of grate. This allowance is largely in excess of what the writer found necessary on his system.

Nevertheless, although the allowance of opening for air above the fuel is apparently far in excess of what is really needful on a subdivided and well-distributed system of supply – much in excess, for instance, of the allowance, 4 square inches per square foot of grate, made by Mr C. W. Williams – the system of the brick arch and the doorway deflector in combination has, in England at least, practically superseded other systems. Its cheapness and its undoubtedly great degree of effectiveness are the qualities by which it has commended itself for general adoption. Yet the economical efficiency of the system for evaporation is open to question. The application of this system is illustrated in the plans of the 'D. Luiz' locomotive, described in detail farther on.

Singularly enough, an effective mixture of the combustible gases with the atmospheric air which is admitted for combustion – that which one has been in the habit of supposing could only be effected in the course of a range of 20 feet or 30 feet in ordinary stationary boilers – can be accomplished in the fire-box of a locomotive within the extent of a travel not exceeding as many inches. That the combustion of coal should be effectually accomplished within such narrow limits as those of an ordinary fire-box is mainly due to the exceptionally powerful draught, the comparatively high temperature which accompanies it, and the forcible intermixture of air admitted from the doorway with the combustible gases, by the simple action of the deflector or baffle-plate. By the rapid draught, a smaller excess of air is required and admitted for effecting complete chemical combustion, than when a mild draught is employed; consequently there is a higher temperature of combustion above the fire. Again, the firebrick arch, heated to a bright redness, reverberates the radiated and converted heat absorbed by it, and maintains a higher

---

3. 'On the Burning of Coal instead of Coke in Locomotive Engines,' in the *Proceedings of the Institution of Mechanical Engineers,* 1860; page 147.

temperature during the varying conditions of the fire. The action, in fact, is, in miniature, what was laboriously effected more than twenty years ago by Mr Joseph Beattie, by means of an elaborate structure of firebricks.

Mr Michael Reynolds, in his instructive work on 'Locomotive Engine Driving', lays down in clear language the conditions for good firing, with coal as fuel, by which the pressure of steam is most easily maintained, and smoke is most effectually prevented. He maintains that a concave fire should be formed, and so kept up, of a form almost resembling the inside of a tea-saucer – shallow and concave – where the thinnest part of the fire is in the centre. The fire is made up, in stoking, close against the walls of the fire-box, and in actual contact with the heating surface; the principal mass of the coals lying over the bearers which carry the fire-bars. The centre of this kind of fire is self-feeding, for, by the action of the blast and the shaking of the engine, the lumps in the corners are caused to roll or fall towards the centre. On this system, the centre is the thinnest part of the fire – quite open and free from ash or clinker. The dirt falls down by the sides of the copper plates, and assists in preventing the cold air from touching the plates. With a fire of this description, the air or oxygen can only get into the fire-box and into the neighbourhood of the tubes, through the centre – through fire – and, mingling with the flame, it becomes instantly heated to a very high temperature before entering the tubes, which are thereby assisted in maintaining an even pressure in the boiler. 'The secret of first-rate firing is to fire frequently, a little at a time. It requires perseverance, but it is the *only way* to accomplish four hours of hard running with anything like success.' Each round of firing should consist of six shovelfuls of coals only, one for each of the four corners of the fire-box, one close to the tube-plate at the middle, and the sixth under the doorway. 'Thus,' says Mr Reynolds, 'every particle of good matter in the coal may be burned up, and the fire may be worked to the highest point of economy.'

The elongated fire-box of Mr J. J. Cudworth, employed in the locomotives of the South-Eastern Railway, is the simplest and most successful of the coal-burning fire-boxes of the third class. The grate is inclined downwards towards the tube-plate, so that the fresh fuel, coal-slack or coking-coal, introduced at the doorway, gradually slides down by gravitation as it is consumed. The fire-box is 7 feet 6 inches long, and the grate is 7 feet long, having a short dead-plate at the upper end, and a clinker-plate for dropping the fire at the lower end, next the tube-plate. The fire-box is divided longitudinally into two parts by a water-space or diaphragm, thus forming two district grates, each 18 inches wide. In the ordinary management of the fire, these grates are stoked alternately, and the steam is easily and well kept up.

It has not been attempted, in the foregoing notice, to describe all the plans that have been designed for the purpose of consuming coal without smoke in locomotives. The intention has been to show generally the directions in which engineers have operated, for the means of effecting complete combustion. There is one feature of considerable importance, which is common to all – the steam blowpipe or auxiliary jet in the chimney.[4]

---

4. For very full illustrated accounts of the various designs of locomotive-furnaces for burning coal, and of the performances of the toilers and engines, see *Railway Locomotives,* 1860, page 25*; a paper on 'Coal-burning and Feed-water Heating in Locomotive Engines', by D. K. Clark, in the *Proceedings of the Institution of Civil Engineers,* 1859–60, vol. xix., page 546; *Locomotive Engineering,* 1871, page 295.

Chapter 6

The Engine

The action of the engine has been noticed in general terms in the descriptive account of Stephenson's early locomotive, page 24. It is the same in principle now, with such modifications as have enabled the locomotive of today to enormously surpass the achievements of the old engine. By the application of lap on the valve, the steam can be cut off, expanded, and exhausted from the cylinder, in the course of the stroke of the piston, whilst the exhaust is kept well open to the atmosphere for the continuous escape of the residue of steam from the cylinder during the return-stroke. By the employment of the link-motion, in conjunction with the lap-valve, a simple means – surpassing in efficiency all the other contrivances that have been employed for the purpose – is supplied for varying the quantity of steam admitted for each stroke of the piston, according to the power required to be exerted, and increasing the degree of expansion of the steam in proportion as it is earlier cut off, at the same time that the steam is effectively exhausted and finally shut up and compressed against the end of the cylinder, in preparation for the admission of steam for the succeeding stroke. Before proceeding farther, the movement of the piston relative to that of the crank, as well as the movement and action of the slide-valve in its relation to that of the piston, had better be explained by the process of geometrical illustration.

Geometrical Illustration of the Movement of the Piston relative to that of the Crank – The piston acts upon and keeps pace with the crank, for every stroke, through the medium of the connecting-rod; and it will have been seen that the varying angularity of the connecting rod influences the movement of the piston in such a manner that the piston moves more slowly during one-half of the stroke – that which is next the crank – than during the other. With an indefinitely long connecting-rod, of which the angularity is inconsiderable, the relation of the motion of the crank and the piston is represented by the annexed diagram, Fig. 26, in which *a c* is the stroke of the piston, and *a b c* the half-revolution of the crank-pin, simultaneously described. Let the path of the crank-pin be divided

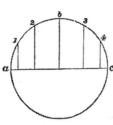

Figure 26. Piston and Crank.

into equal parts at the points 1, 2, 3, 4, and draw verticals from the points of division to the line *a c*; then, as the angular speed of the crank-pin is uniform, and the divisions of the circular path *a b c* are equal, the line *a c* is divided, by the perpendiculars already drawn, into segments representing spaces described by the piston in equal times, and therefore also the varying average velocity of the piston in traversing these spaces. Whence it is obvious that the speed of the piston, during one stroke, begins and ends at nothing at the extreme or dead points, *a, c*; that it accelerates towards *b,* the position at half-stroke, where it reaches a maximum, and that beyond this point it is retarded till it gains the end of its stroke. The two halves of the stroke are described in equal times, and in these halves the variations of the velocity of the piston are exact counterparts.

The connecting-rod has been supposed to be indefinitely long, to consist with the supposition that the piston keeps pace exactly with the movement of the crank-pin in the direction of the centre-line of the engine, between one end of the stroke and the other.

The obliquity of the connecting-rod destroys the symmetry here described. In a stroke of the piston, there are three cardinal points – the commencement, the middle, and the termination of the stroke. According to the preceding diagram, these three points are arrived at by the piston simultaneously with the horizontal and vertical positions of the crank. But the angularity of the connecting-rod at half-stroke of the piston, virtually shortens its length, and the crank-pin is, by as much, short of its midway position.

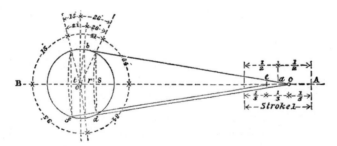

Figure 27. Piston, Connecting-rod, and Crank.

As the crank-pin is presumed to move with a uniform angular velocity, it follows that the piston describes the two halves of its stroke with different average velocities, and in unequal times. In an engine, for instance, with a stroke of 24 inches, having the crank 1 foot long, and the connecting-rod 5 feet long, or five times the length of the crank, it is found from the annexed diagram, Fig. 27, of the relative positions of the piston and the crank, that at half-stroke of the piston the connecting-rod, *a b*, falls short of the vertical centre-line of the crank by the amount, *o r*. Dividing the stroke of the piston into three equal parts, the connecting-rod being in the relative positions, *c d, e f,* the distances of the points, *d, f,* from the centre-line, are *o s, o t,* respectively about 3 inches and 5 inches. The corresponding angular positions of the crank are, for the half-stroke of the piston, 6° with the vertical, and for the one-third of the stroke respectively 14° and 24½. The sum of 14° and 24½°, or 38½°, is the angular motion of the crank during the middle third of the stroke, and the complements of those, 76° and 65°, are the angular motions for the extreme thirds. The average speed of the piston, therefore, in describing the successive thirds of its stroke in the direction *a c,* are inversely as 76, 38½, 65½, or directly as 1, 2, 1.16 nearly; and the two halves of the whole stroke are described with average speeds inversely as 96° to 84°, or directly as 7 to 8. The shorter the connecting-rod, the greater is the irregularity so introduced in the motion of the piston.

Motion and Action of the Slide-valve in relation to tie Motion of the Piston – As the path of the crank-pin is represented by a circle, and the stroke of the piston by a straight line equal to the diameter of that circle, so also the path of the excentric is represented by a circle, and the travel of the slide-valve by a straight line equal to the diameter of the circle of the excentric: assuming, for the sake of illustration, that the valve is actuated in direct connection with the excentric. If, then, two circles be described on a common centre, *c,* Fig. 28, for the crank-path and the excentric-path respectively, their diameters, A B, a b, are the stroke of the piston and the travel of the valve. When the piston is at one end of the stroke, at D E, the valve is opening the port at *a',* and is just as much in advance of its middle position over the ports, as is needed to draw the lap clear off the edge of the port at *a',* in addition to the lead or opening of the port at the beginning of the stroke. The position of the excentric, then, represented by its own revolving centre, must be at the point *a',* which is in advance of its middle position, in the line D E, by as much as the

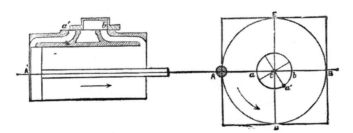

Figure 28. Piston and Slide-valve.

lap plus the lead. As the axle revolves, the valve is farther opened by the retiring excentric, till it falls into the line A B, when the crank is getting on to half-stroke. When the crank has attained to half-stroke, in the position *c* D, the excentric is on its way returning, and the motion of the valve is reversed on the way to close the port. The port is actually closed some time before the valve and the excentric return to their midway position – the former over the ports, and the latter in the line *c* E – in virtue of the lap on the valve. Further, when the valve and the excentric do arrive at their middle positions of half-travel and half-stroke, the edge of the cavity of the valve coincides with the inner edge of the steam-port; and the opening of the port to the exhaust-passage through the medium of the cavity is forthwith established by the progressive motion of the valve. All that has just been described of the operation of the excentric on the valve is effected before the crank completes a half revolution; that is, before the crank-pin arrives at the point B, and, consequently, completes its stroke. The valve, indeed, makes another change before this. It opens the other port at *b'*, for the other end of the cylinder, the lap having been completely withdrawn, and an additional movement for the lead effected, just as the stroke is completed.

The successive positions occupied by the valve during a revolution of the crank may be graphically represented, as in Fig. 29, where A B and *a b*, being the circles of the crank and the excentric respectively, are divided into any equal number of parts, of which the points A, *a'*, are respectively the positions of the crank and the excentric at the beginning of the stroke; the other points, B, *b'*, D, *d'*, E, *e'*, show the simultaneous positions of the crank and the excentric, at intervals of one-fourth of a revolution. Draw the lines *e, f, g, h, i, k,* parallel to the centre-line *a b,* spaced apart at intervals equal to the exhaust-port and the steam-

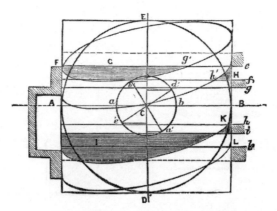

Figure 29. Diagram of Valve-motion.

ports, and the intervening bars; *e f* and *i k* being the steam-ports, and *g h* the exhaust-port. Place the valve on the perpendicular at A, in the right position with respect to the parallels *e, f, k,* for the commencement of the stroke, showing the requisite lead at F, and set off its position on the face of the diagram, according with the position of the crank. The elliptic lines, traced so as to connect these positions, represent the linear motion of the valve, relative to the ports and to the crank; and, with the aid of a little shading, they clearly show the successive periods and changes of the distribution, subject, of course, to correction for the varying irregularity of the connecting-rod. The shaded space, o, shows the period of admission, terminating at *g'*; and the shaded space, h, the period of exhaustion, commencing at *h'*. The shaded space, I, shows the exhaustion for the alternate end of the cylinder; K, the compression; and L, the short period of pre- admission of steam for the following stroke.

On the same system, diagrams of motion may be constructed for any other proportions or for any other species of valve, whether double or superposed valves, under any special conditions of movement. The link-motion, as a variable-expansion gear, operates for varying the cut-off and the degree of expansion by varying the travel of the valve; the diminished cut-off and the prolonged expansion being together effected by the shortening of the travel. The result is precisely the same as if an excentric of a correspondingly shorter throw were substituted for an excentric of greater throw. It can be readily understood, on inspecting the diagram of motion, Fig. 29, that for a shorter travel of valve, a series of flatter ellipses of movement would be traced, which would intersect the parallel lines of the ports at earlier points of the stroke represented by the length, A B.

That the compound movement of the valve produced by the combined action of two excentrics – the fore excentric and the aft excentric – should be itself of the nature of the motion produced by a simple excentric is natural enough; and all the movements of a slide-valve, with its action on the steam – the 'distribution' as the total result is usually called – may be readily ascertained when the travel of a valve actuated by the link-motion is known. The distribution is, in fact, that which would be due to the employment of a simple excentric having an equal length of travel directly connected to the valve. Thus, the mystery of the link-motion, if it ever existed, is explained.[5]

The link-motion, as originally employed by Mr Stephenson, is shown by centre-lines in Fig. 30. The crank is shown at one end of the stroke, opposed by the fore excentric, *a,* and the back excentric, *a'*. From these

5. The writer proved diagramatically the identity of the action of the link-motion with that of simple excentrics in *Railway Machinery,* 1855, p. 48.

proceed the fore-excentric rod, *b,* and the back-excentric rod, *b'.* They are connected at the ends to the expansion-link, *c,* so formed as to receive a sliding-block on the end of the valve-rod guide, *g.* The link is supported by a jointed bar, *k,* pinned to the end of the lever, *h,* on the reversing shaft, *i;* and it is shifted downwards or upwards from the middle position given in the diagram, by an appropriate movement of the reversing shaft. It is thence called the 'shifting link'. When it is lowered so as to bring the fore-excentric rod, *b,* into a line with the valve-rod and guide, *g,* or nearly so, the valve is fully under the control of the fore excentric, for forward gear; and, on the contrary, when the link is shifted upwards, so as to place the valve directly under the action of the back-excentric rod, *b',* it is in back-gear. The link may also be shifted to any intermediate position in fore-gear or in back-gear; and variable cut-off and expansion

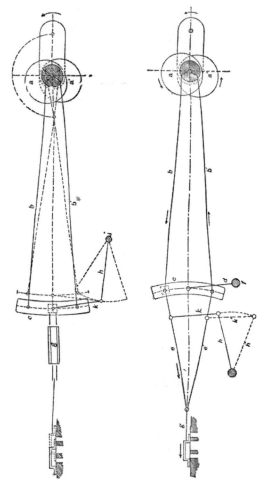

Figure 30. Stephenson's
Link-motion.

Figure 31. Stationary
Link-motion.

may thus be effected. The corresponding position of the link-motion, when the crank is at the other end of its stroke, is shown by dot-lining.

There is another form of link-motion, known as the 'stationary link', shown in centre-lines in Fig. 31, so called because the link, *c,* is supported direct by a bar, *d,* upon a fixed shaft, *f,* and the changing of the gear is effected by moving a radius-link, *e,* connected with the valve-rod, *g,* and to the slide-block, upwards and downwards in the link. The curvature of the link is necessarily reversed – adapted to the radial movements of the valve-rod link. The valve-rod link is supported by the bar, *k,* moved by the lever, *h,* on the reversing shaft, *i.*

There is a third form of link-motion – a combination, in effect, of the first and second link-motion – the invention of Mr Alexander Allan, shown in the illustrations of the 'D. Luiz' farther on. For reversing and for effecting variable expansion, both the expansion-link and the valve-rod-link are shifted by one movement of the reversing shaft in opposite directions, one upwards, the other downwards. By this means reversing may be effected with only half the vertical range of movement necessary when the movement is applied to only one of the pieces. In this case the link is straight, and therefore the gearing is called the 'straight-link motion'.

By means of any of these link-motions a very excellent 'distribution' of steam may be effected. Other systems of valve-gear for variable expansion have been and are now employed in locomotives; but it is a fact that the link-motion stands first in efficiency and in general excellence.

With the link-motion, acting upon well-proportioned valves, it may be reckoned that, generally, the period of admission of steam to the cylinder may be varied from 75 per cent, to 12 per cent, of the stroke, whilst the steam is expanded to, and exhausted at, from 91 per cent, to 50 per cent, of the stroke. These distributions are effected by employing a slide-valve, having a travel of 4½ inches, a lap of 1 inch, and a lead of $5/16$ inch.

Chapter 7

Action of Steam in the Cylinder

The movements of the slide-valve and the distribution of the steam having been considered geometrically, it remains to verify these by the aid of the indicator – an instrument by means of which, as a sort of stethoscope, the action of the steam in the cylinder may be perceived and registered with minuteness, and with a high degree of exactness. For the purpose of measuring the pressure by the indicator, a small piston is movable in a small cylinder, one end of which is in direct communication with one end of the interior of the steam-cylinder, the other end of the small cylinder of the instrument being open to the atmosphere. In M'Naught's indicator the piston is fully $^3/_8$ inch in diameter, having an area of $^1/_8$ square inch. The pressure on the piston is resisted by a helical spring, the tension of which increases at the rate of 40lbs per square inch of pressure to the inch of rise. In the Richards indicator a short spring is employed, and the range is multiplied by means of a lever. The pressure is recorded by a pencil connected with the spring, which is placed in contact with a sheet of paper lapped upon a cylinder, which is made to revolve backwards and forwards in unison with the strokes of the engine-piston. The writer, in 1849 and 1850, made experimental investigations of the behaviour and conditions of steam in locomotive-engines, the results of which were published in 1852.[6] Since the publication of these investigations, comprising an original experimental demonstration of the great loss of steam by condensation in the cylinder when attempted to be worked expansively, the subject has been frequently revived. The writer's original conclusions have been verified in various ways, and the necessity for the application of the steam-jacket, or equivalent means of maintaining or contributing to maintain, the expanding steam at a suitable temperature, is now generally acknowledged.[7]

---

6. *Proceedings of the Institution of Mechanical Engineers*, 1852, and in *Railway Machinery in* 1851–53.
7. In an article on 'Utilisation of Steam and Compound Cylinders in Locomotives', by M. A. Mallet, in the *Compte Rendu de la Société des Ingénieurs Civils*, 1877 (page 852), M. Mallet, after having referred to a remarkable forecast by M. Combes, states: 'Mr D. K. Clark was the first experimentalist who, by

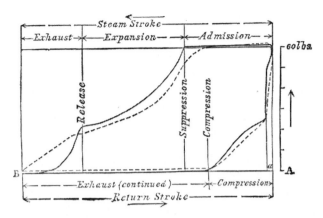

Figure 32. Indicator-diagrams.

To illustrate the function and the utility of the indicator, as well as the action of the steam in the cylinder, for one stroke of the piston, examples of indicator-diagrams, taken by the writer in 1850, from one of the cylinders of a locomotive, are shown in Fig. 32. The base line, A B, is the line of atmospheric pressure, and represents the stroke of the piston; and the rectangular space above it may be supposed to be the interior of the cylinder. The heavy-line figure is a diagram of the action of the steam, when the piston is moved in the cylinder at an average speed of 40 feet per minute, and shows by its angularity how the steam is controlled by the valve, and the precise points of the stroke at which the changes of the distribution take place. The piston is represented as having started from the right-hand end of the cylinder, under a uniform pressure of 61lbs per square inch. It is expanded till the pressure falls to 23lbs at the point

---

practical evidence, traced to its true cause the excess of the quantity of steam, or the water-equivalent of it, in the cylinder, at the end of the expansion, over the quantity at the beginning of the expansion.' 'He demonstrated that a portion of the steam when admitted at each stroke was condensed, and that it was in part re-evaporated at the end of the expansion; and that, by this destroying process, the efforts at economy by cutting-off early and expanding, were baffled, insomuch that it was practically impossible with economy, to cut off earlier than at one-third of the stroke.' M. Mallet proceeds to say:– 'In these publications [those already mentioned in the previous foot-note] has been for the first time so completely elucidated the behaviour of the steam in the cylinder of locomotives, and the part that is played by the condensation of the steam during the admission – a characteristic phenomenon which gives the key of the difference which always exists between the practical expanditure of engines and the calculated consumptions, and the reality of which, strange to say, many engineers, otherwise very distinguished, really believed could be contested, ten or twelve years after the publication of those works.'

of release, where it is exhausted into the atmosphere, and it arrives at atmospheric pressure by the time the piston reaches the end of the stroke, at B.

Now, how is the behaviour of the steam modified according to the speed of the piston? The dot-line diagram illustrates the action of the steam in the same cylinder, when the piston moved at an average speed of 310 feet per minute. The steam enters at an initial pressure of 62lbs per square inch; but it suffers a slight reduction of pressure as the piston recedes before it; but it is only when the piston nears the point of suppression, and the port is nearly closed by the valve, that the pressure rapidly falls in the diagram towards the line when the steam is cut off. This is a case of simple wire-drawing, as the opening of the port, previously wide enough to admit all the steam that could find its way into the cylinder against the frictional resistance and the bends of the passage, is now reduced to the minimum width consistent with this condition, and a further contraction, and final closing of the opening, necessarily occasion an accelerated fall of the pressure, which at the point of cut-off is only 54lbs above the atmosphere, although it was 62lbs at the beginning of the stroke. The pressure falls during the expansion of the steam, to 19lbs per square inch, when the steam is exhausted, and it reaches 2lbs per square inch at the end of the stroke. The curve of expansion, it appears, runs into those of the admission and the exhaust, without any of the abruptness which distinguishes the slow diagram; the fact being that expansion had virtually begun before the steam was nominally cut off – a result implied in the action of wire-drawing; and there was, therefore, not the same liability to sudden change of pressure on entering the period of expansion. At the termination of the period of expansion the curve crosses the exhaust-line nearly at right angles, and barely reaches the minimum pressure when it arrives at the termination of the stroke. This minimum pressure, 2lbs per square inch, is continued during the return-stroke, and is caused by imperfect exhaustion, when the speed of the returning piston was such that it was necessary to raise a pressure of 2lbs by the piston upon the steam, to drive it out.

Adducing the evidence of the indicator in analysing the behaviour of steam in cylinders under different conditions, the indicator-diagrams, Figs. 33 and 34, were taken from one of the cylinders of the 'Great Britain' locomotive, on the Great Western Railway.[8] The cylinders were 18 inches in diameter, with a stroke of 24 inches; the steam ports were 13 inches long

8. Reproduced from the writer's paper on 'Expansive Working of Steam in Locomotives', in *Proceedings of the Institution of Mechanical Engineers*, 1852; page 60.

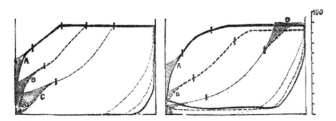

Figures 33–34. Indicator-diagrams from the 'Great Britain' Locomotive.

by 2 inches wide; and the exhaust port 13 inches by 3½ inches wide. The lap of the valve was 1¼ inch at each end outside, and ¹/₁₆ inch inside. The driving-wheels were 8 feet in diameter. Each figure shows three diagrams for periods of admission of steam, respectively 16 inches, 11¾ inches, and 7 inches of the stroke; or 66²/₃ per cent., 49 per cent., and 30 per cent.; the terminations of which, and of the expansions, are pointed out on the diagrams. For the first figure, the speed of piston was 240 feet per minute; for the second, 770 feet per minute: corresponding respectively to speeds on the railway of 17 and 55 miles per hour. The wire-drawing at the lower speed obviously was nothing; at the higher speed, the pressure fell 3lbs, 12lbs, and 25lbs below the initial pressure before the steam was cut-off. The falling off of the pressure was doubtless to be accounted for by the fact that, in the three eases, the travels of the valves were respectively 4¾ inches, 3¹⁵/₁₆ inches, and 3⁷/₁₆ inches; whilst the maximum opening of the port was 1¹/₃₂ inch, ¹¹/₁₆ inch nearly, and ½ inch. But it was found that, even in the third case, with the shortest admission, and when the maximum opening of the port was only ½ inch, the steam-line was practically straight and parallel to the atmospheric line, at speeds of piston up to 450 feet per minute. This is an example of the fact, which is constantly exemplified in practice, that the maximum opening of the port allowed by the valve, though it may be much less than the total width of the port, is sufficiently wide to pass all the steam that can force its way along the passage ; and that no more steam could be passed through, under the circumstances, even if the port were thrown wide open to the steam in the valve-chest.

When steam is admitted into the cylinder while the cylinders are comparatively cold, or less hot than the steam, a very sensible degree of condensation of the steam takes place during the admission in the process of heating the cylinder to the temperature of the steam, which continues to a certain extent during the period of expansion. A portion of this abstracted heat, though but a small fraction, passes off and is lost; the remainder is retained by the cylinder, until it is re-absorbed by the precipitated steam, during the expansion of the remaining steam, if the expansion be continued far enough; that is to say, until the temperature of the expanding steam falls below that of the cylinder. This is a destructive process, occasioning an absolute loss of steam; and the amount of steam thus wastefully precipitated, and but partially revived, increases rapidly in proportion as the steam is cut-off earlier, and expansion is extended. In the cylinders of ordinary locomotives, the extra consumption and waste of steam devoted, in this way, to the heating of the cylinder in the first part of the stroke, is above 12 per cent, of the whole steam consumed, when the steam is cut-off at one-third. In exposed locomotive-cylinders, the loss is proved to amount to nearly 40 per cent, of the whole steam consumed, when cut-off at one-eighth of the stroke.

This important species of loss is inseparable from the attempt to work steam expansively, when there is not any special provision for the heating of the cylinder, and maintaining it at a suitably high temperature, equal at least to the initial temperature of the steam. The magnitude of the loss is so great as to defeat all such attempts at economy of fuel and steam, by expansive working; and it affords a sufficient explanation of the fact, in engineering practice, that expansive working has been found to be expensive working, and that in many cases an absolutely greater quantity of fuel has been consumed in extended expansive working, while less power has been actually developed.[9]

In no part of the distribution is the advantage of time so evident as during the period of exhaust. It is plain, by reference to Figs. 33 and 34, page 85, that the steam does not discharge itself instantly from the cylinder, at the point of release or exhaust, for in all the diagrams the piston visibly travels through some distance before the pressure falls to a minimum. In the left-hand figure, at the lower speed, the piston moves 3½ inches from the point at which the steam is released, to the point at which the pressure falls to the atmospheric line. At the higher speed, in the right-hand cylinder, the steam only reaches the minimum pressure of 2lbs, when the piston has reached to the end of the stroke, through 5 inches of the cylinder.

The compression of the exhaust-steam, which takes place after it is shut up, against the end of the cylinder, is of indispensable service in opposing a powerful resistance for the neutralizing of the momentum of the reciprocating masses of the piston and its connections. There is, of course, a deduction made by the compressive resistance of the steam, from the net work done by the steam for each stroke of the piston. This is a matter of but secondary importance, and it is much more to the point to observe that compression, whilst it occasions a reduction of the available power, also returns a portion of the exhaust-steam, to take its part in working again in the next steam-stroke of the piston: thus, to a great extent – in some cases altogether –

9. See *Railway Machinery*, 1855, pages 63 to 109, for an exhaustive experimental investigation of the action of steam in locomotive-engines.

compensating for the reduction of power by a corresponding reduction of the quantity of steam consumed. Moreover, it is found, on analysis, that the earlier the steam is cut-off, and the greater the degree of expansion, the conditions of economy require that the earlier also should the compression of the exhaust-steam be commenced in the course of the return stroke.

The extent of the influence of wiredrawing, and of the opening of the exhaust for the escape of the expanding steam, before the piston has arrived at the end of the stroke, may be estimated from the diagrams, Figs. 33 and 34. To show what the form of the diagrams would have been, if the steam had not been released, and the expansion had been continued to the end of the stroke, the shaded spaces, A, B, C, are added to the several diagrams. The extensions of the expansion-curves are easily calculated for the purpose, in terms of the relative volumes of steam, from the pressures indicated at the points of exhaust. The shaded areas, A, B, C, comprised between the exhaust curves actually described, and the extensions of the expansion lines, express the quantities of work lost by exhausting the steam before the stroke is completed. The effective mean pressures for each of the six diagrams are here given, together with the deductions for loss by early exhaust, averaged for the whole stroke:

Effective mean pressure per square inch:

Speed of Locomotive	17 miles per hour.	55 miles per hour.
Cut-off $66^2/_3$ per cent	77.5lb	67.6lb
Cut-off 49 per cent	66.1lb	50.8lb
Cut-off 30 per cent	43.5lb	29.4lb

Loss of pressure per square inch, by early exhaust:

Cut-off $66^2/_3$ per cent	$^7/_8$lb	1lb
Cut-off 49 per cent	$2^1/_4$lb	1lb
Cut-off 30 per cent	$3^1/_8$lb	$^3/_8$lb

The losses are here seen to be, at the higher speed, very small, merely nominal; and, curiously enough, the loss by the earlier exhaust, for a cut-off of 30 per cent., is actually less at the higher speed than the loss for a cut-off of $66^2/_3$ per cent. The shorter cut-offs are only practised at high speeds, and the loss by them at low speeds is of no practical moment.

This is not all. The early exhaust co-operates in effecting a complete exhaust for the return-stroke against the atmosphere, and keeping down, if not entirely preventing, any excess of back-pressure above the pressure of the atmosphere.

The reduction of pressure by wiredrawing, equally, is unimportant. Wiredrawing, to a material extent, only takes place according to the indicator-diagrams, Figs. 33 and 34, at high speeds, and with very short periods of admission. The shaded space, D, bounded by a prolongation upwards of the expansion-line for 30 per cent, of admission, represents the whole possible loss by wire-drawing, and it amounts to an average reduction of 1lb per square inch of pressure for the whole of the stroke. But this is only the result of what virtually takes place in wiredrawing, which is, to a great extent, equivalent to an earlier cutting-off, and a greater degree of expansion.

The effective mean pressure in ordinary steam-cylinders, non-condensing, worked by ordinary slide-valves and link-motion, is given in the annexed table, for various periods of admission of from 10 per cent, to 75 per cent, of the stroke, and for maximum pressures in the cylinder, of from 60lbs per square inch to 150lbs per square inch.[10]

Effective Mean Pressure in the Locomotive-Cylinder.

Period of Admission, in parts of the stroke.	Effective mean pressure, in parts of maximum pressure.	Period of Admission, as a fraction of the stroke.	Effective mean pressure, as a fraction of the maximum pressure.
Per cent.	Per cent.		
10	15	1-10th	1-7th fully.
12½	20	1-8th	1-5th
15	24	1-6th	1-4th
17½	28	1-6th	1-4th
20	32	1-5th	1-3rd
25	40	1-4th	2-5ths
30	46	1-3rd	1-2nd
35	52	1-3rd	1-2nd
40	57		
45	62		
50	67	1-2nd	2-3rds
55	72		
60	77		
65	81	2-3rds	4-5ths
70	85		
75	89	3-4ths	9-10ths

10. This table is copied from *Railway Machinery*, 1855; page 116.

Locomotion number 1, 0-4-0 tender locomotive, Stockton & Darlington Railway, designed by George Stephenson and constructed in 1825. Locomotion hauled the first passenger train on a public railway in the world, on the opening day of the S&DR, 27 September 1825. This locomotive is now preserved at North Road Station, Darlington.

Puffing Billy, 2-2-0 tender locomotive, designed by William Headley and constructed at Wylam Colliery in 1813. This locomotive is now part of the National Collection and is on display at York.

Agenoria, 0-4-0 tender locomotive, Shutt End Colliery Railway, constructed by Foster Rastrick & Co in 1829. An almost identical sister locomotive named *Stourbridge Lion* was constructed for export to the USA and became the first locomotive to be shipped to that continent.

Invicta, 0-4-0 tender locomotive, Canterbury & Whitstable Railway, designed by George Stephenson, constructed in 1829. This locomotive is now on display at Canterbury Museum.

Rocket, 2-2-0 tender locomotive, Liverpool & Manchester Railway, later sold to Lord Carlisle's Railway. Designed by Robert Stephenson and constructed in 1829, with a water tube boiler designed by Henry Booth. Rocket won the competition for the best locomotive at the Rainhill Trials, held in 1829, winning a £500 prize. The locomotive is now preserved at the Science Museum, London, where it is exhibited in its later rebuilt condition as seen here.

The replica of *North Star*, constructed in 1935 for the centenary of the Great Western Railway. The original locomotive was constructed to 5ft-6in gauge in 1837, as an export for the New Orleans Railway in the USA. As the order for America was cancelled, the locomotive was re-gauged to Broad Gauge and sold to the Great Western, where it hauled the first train in 1838. The original *North Star* was withdrawn in 1870 and preserved at Swindon works until 1906, when it was broken up for scrap. A number of parts from the original locomotive survived in store and were used in the construction of the 1935 replica. *North Star* is now on display at the Steam Museum, Swindon.

The 1935 constructed replica of the Stephenson 2-2-2 tender locomotive, *Adler*, which is now part of the German national collection. The original locomotive was constructed at the Stephenson Works in Newcastle in 1835, for the first railway in Germany.

Built in 1835 for the Liverpool and Manchester Railway.
The first engine with inside cylinders.

OLD PASSENGER LOCOMOTIVE
DRIVING WHEELS 5 FT. DIAMETER

A London & Birmingham Bury 2-2-0 passenger tender locomotive, constructed in 1835 for the opening of the line. Bury Locomotives had bar, rather than plate frames and were constructed in the early years of railway development. There are two examples preserved in the British isles, the Furness Railway 0-4-0 tender locomotive *Copper Nob*, at the National Railway Museum, York, and Great Southern & Western Railway 2-2-2 tender locomotive number 36, at Kent station, Cork, in Ireland.

Liverpool & Manchester Railway 0-4-2 tender baggage locomotive, *Lion*, constructed by Todd Kitson & Laird in 1837. After withdrawal, it was sold to the Mersey Docks and Harbour Board, where it became a pumping engine. *Lion* was rescued in 1928, by the Liverpool Engineering Society and restored by the LMS in time for the centenary of the Liverpool & Manchester Railway in 1930. *Lion* has appeared in several feature films including the *Titfield Thunderbolt*, an Ealing comedy. The locomotive is now preserved in the Liverpool Museum, where it has pride of place in the main gallery.

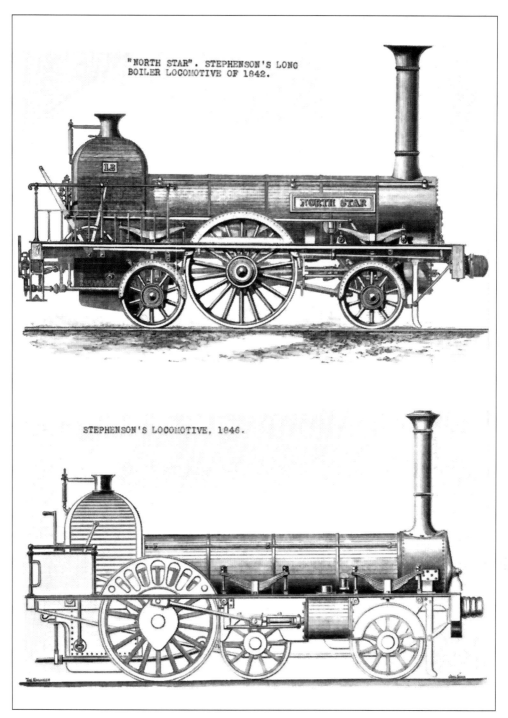

"NORTH STAR". STEPHENSON'S LONG
BOILER LOCOMOTIVE OF 1842.

NORTH STAR

STEPHENSON'S LOCOMOTIVE, 1846.

Two examples of Stephenson locomotives constructed in the 1840s. Above, Long boiler 2-2-2 tender passenger locomotive, *North Star*, with a Haycock firebox and domeless boiler, constructed in 1842. Below, we have a Crampton-type 4-2-0 tender passenger locomotive, again fitted with a haycock firebox and domeless boiler, constructed in 1846.

A Crewe type 2-2-2 tender passenger locomotive, designed by Buddicombe and Alexander Allan, constructed in 1846. *Columbine*, the sole surviving member of this famous class of passenger locomotive, is preserved as part of the National Collection.

The Crewe type mixed traffic 2-4-0 tender locomotive, designed by Buddicombe and Alexander Allan, constructed in 1846. A number of these locomotives were rebuilt as 2-4-0T locomotives in the 1860s and survived in service until the late 1890s to early 1900s.

London Brighton & South Coast Railway, Craven Period 2-2-2 tender passenger locomotive, number 292, *Seaford*, here seen in Stroudley livery c1875. This locomotive has some interesting features, including a haycock firebox and domeless boiler. The gong on the side of the tender is part of the emergency alarm system, in use before the communication cord, attached to the train braking system.

Great Western Railway, Gooch broad gauge 4-2-2 tender express locomotive, *Hirondelle*. Constructed in 1848, this locomotive was one of a large number of highly successful machines that hauled the most important long-distance express trains to the west of England, South Wales and the West Midlands, from the 1840s until the demise of the broad gauge in 1892. *Hirondelle*, was withdrawn and broken up in 1873, however locomotives of a similar, more modern design, the Rover class 4-2-2 tender locomotives, continued in service until 1892.

0-4-0WT *Queen* constructed in 1852 by E.B. Wilson and purchased in 1868 by the broad gauge Torbay and Brixham Railway. *Queen* is an example of a number of small 0-4-0WT locomotives constructed by E.B. Wilson for main line companies and use by contractors during the mid-nineteenth century. *Queen* was withdrawn, on takeover of the Torbay and Brixham Railway, by the Great Western in 1883.

Wantage Tramway Number 5, *Jane*, an 0-4-0WT constructed by George England at Hatcham iron works, London, in 1857. This locomotive was originally supplied to the Sandy and Potton Railway in Bedfordshire and named *Shannon*, after the frigate once commanded by Captain William Peel RN, who was Sir Robert Peel's third son. Captain Peel RN was the principal local land owner, for the formation from Sandy to Potton and paid for the construction of both the railway and its rolling stock. The S & PR was taken over in 1860, by the Bedford and Cambridge Railway, later a part of the LNWR. *Shannon* became LNWR number 1104 and was later sold in 1878 to the Wantage Tramway in Berkshire, where she worked until the tramway closed in 1945. In 1946, the Great Western purchased the locomotive for preservation at Wantage Road station. After the station closed in 1965, the locomotive was relocated to Didcot Railway Centre, in the care of the Great Western Society, as part of the National Collection.

South Devon Railway, broad gauge 4-4-0ST, *Hawk*, constructed in 1859. This classic broad gauge 4-4-0ST was taken into Great Western stock in 1876, when it was renumbered 2108, being withdrawn from service and broken up in 1885.

London & North Western Railway, Bloomer 2-2-2 Passenger tender locomotive, number 1007, *President*, designed by John Ramsbottom and constructed in 1861. These large 2-2-2 tender express locomotives hauled the main express trains on the west coast main line, often heading some of the most important trains, including the Irish Mail train services. Both the large Bloomers and small Bloomers, remained in top link service until the late 1870s when newer classes of express locomotive became available, to replace them on the longer heavier trains.

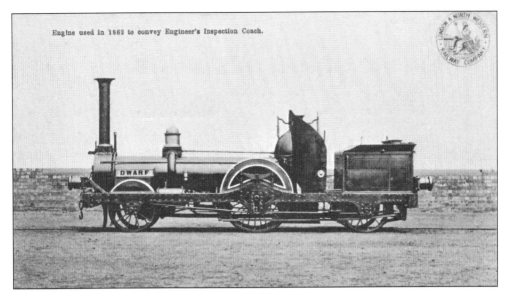

George England 1862 constructed 2-2-2 WT, *Dwarf*. These long wheelbase locomotives, were used by the LNWR for engineering work, especially on ballast trains. The London & North Western Railway had a small fleet of these George England constructed locomotives, which were in service from the early 1860s until the early 1880s, on permanent way department duties.

District Railway, *Beyer Peacock*, A class condensing 4-4-0T number 44, c1869. These highly successful 4-4-0T locomotives, were supplied to both the Metropolitan and the Metropolitan & District Railways. The design was also supplied to other main line companies who operated in London, including the Midland, LNWR and LSWR, who used them on suburban train services, both in London and elsewhere, on their networks. After use in London, some of these locomotives found a new lease of life on other main line railways and on some industrial railways, after withdrawal by the Underground companies. The last A class 4-4-0T number L 45 was withdrawn by London Transport in 1945 and was restored to its original condition as Metropolitan number 23 in 1963, for the Underground centenary. It is now on display at Covent Garden, in the London Transport Museum.

Cambrian Railway, Sharp Stuart constructed 0-6-0 tender goods number 6, *Marquis*, here seen in its black lined out livery, c1878. Sharp Stuart originally constructed locomotives in Manchester; however their business was so successful that they later relocated to Glasgow, where they eventually became a main constituent of the North British Locomotive Company. The Sharp Stuart standard goods was supplied to number of main line companies, including The Cambrian Railway in mid- and north Wales, The Furness Railway in Cumbria and a number were supplied to overseas railways in the 1860s and 1870s.

Great Western Railway, *Armstrong*, outside frame 0-6-0 tender goods, number 1084, here photographed at Westbourne Park, London, c1890. The *Armstrong* goods was a very successful locomotive, with examples being constructed at Swindon and Wolverhampton, where they were painted in a distinctive blue livery. During the Great War, some of these locomotives were acquired by the War Department, for use overseas, being supplied to the ROD in Salonika, Greece. The last members of the class were withdrawn in the early 1930s, making them a long-lived class.

South Eastern Railway, Cudworth, 2-2-2 Tender Mail class locomotive number 81, constructed in 1866 at Ashford Works. This class of locomotive was used on the most important trains on the South Eastern Railway, including the Mail and Continental Boat trains. Note, the coal-burning fire box and the simple vacuum brake equipment attached to the smoke box.

The Prototype, London Chatham & Dover Railway, Large Scotchman class 0-4-2T, *Albion*, here seen at Battersea in London, c1878. The Large Scotchman 0-4-2T locomotives, were used on London local services from the city terminal stations and on branch lines in Kent, where they worked out their days until replaced by more modern motive power in the late 1890s. These locomotives had Spartan open cabs when constructed in 1872, note the basic weatherboard and large open coal bunker. These domeless boilered, inside-framed 0-4-2WT locomotives were based on a similar design produced for the Great Northern Railway by Patrick Stirling during this period.

London & South Western Railway, Joseph Beattie, 2-4-0 Vesuvius Class, tender passenger locomotive. These locomotives were constructed in London at Nine Elms Works, between 1859-68, for use on the main top link trains on the L&SWR. The class was later modified by William Adams who had them re-boilered and modified, which gave them an extension of life in to the early years of the twentieth century. This example of the class is shown in its almost original condition, with its copper- caped chimney, flywheel water pump, before injectors were fitted, which meant that the locomotive had to be moved periodically to pump water in to the boiler. The 1850s and early 1860s were an interesting period of locomotive development when most railways were going over from coke, to coal burning.

Burry Port & Gwendreth Valley Railway, Robert Fairlie designed 0-4-0 0-4-0 articulated tank locomotive, *Mountaineer*. A large number of Fairlie locomotives were constructed from the 1860s until the early 1880s, mostly for export, including sizable numbers for New Zealand and Russia. The most famous railway in Britain to use these locomotives, being the 2ft narrow gauge Festiniog Railway in north Wales, which has used these machines since the 1860s. The Burry Port & Gwendreth Valley Railway used two types of double Fairlie, having four and six coupled machines. This example, *Mountaineer*, has an overseas export look about it, with its open tropical cab and high-running plates. The Fairlie locomotive remained popular on overseas railways, until the first decades of the twentieth century, with some of the last orders going to Mexico.

Probably the most beautiful locomotives from the mid-Victorian period, are Patrick Starlings 8ft 4-2-2 single express passenger locomotives. The Stirling singles were introduced in 1870 and constructed at the Great Northern Railways Doncaster Works. The class hauled the most important trains on the east coast main line, including the 10.00 *Scotch Express*, later known as *The Flying Scotsman*. As trains became heavier the 8ft singles were cascaded to other duties, including stopping services on secondary lines. The last members of the class were not withdrawn until the middle years of the Great War, by which time there were enough newer locomotives to replace them in traffic. The Great Northern Railway had the vision to preserve locomotive number 1, which is now on display in the National Collection at York Railway Museum.

London Brighton & South Coast Railway Stroudley A 1 0-6-0T number 81, *Beulah*, here seen in its original condition, painted in the Stroudley improved engine green livery. Introduced in 1872 and constructed at Brighton Works, the A 1 0-6-0T locomotives were known as Terriers, by the enginemen and later by enthusiasts for many generations. A large proportion of the class of fifty locomotives, were rebuilt under the direction of D. Earl Marsh from 1911 onwards, such was their usefulness on the Brighton line. Some members of the class found a new lease of life, on light railways and in industry, after being sold out of service by the LB&SCR. At least half the class survived to be taken into stock by the Southern in 1923 and smaller number survived to be nationalised in 1948. The last Terriers were withdrawn by British Railways in November 1963, after the closure of the Hayling Island branch. There are ten members of the class preserved, including number 82 *Boxhill* at National Railway Museum, York, and number 54 *Waddon*, preserved at the Canadian National Railway Museum, Delson, Montreal.

North Eastern Railway, William Bouch designed long boilered 0-6-0 tender goods number 1275, constructed by Dubs in Glasgow in 1874. This locomotive was originally owned by the Stockton & Darlington Railway and was later taken in to NER stock, being withdrawn at the grouping in 1923. 1275, was restored in time for the centenary celebrations in 1925, of the S&DR at Shildon. The locomotive represents a long line of machines of this type going back to the 1840s, when the long boilered locomotives were first introduced. 1275, is part of the National Collection and is preserved and on display at Darlington North Road Station Museum.

London Brighton & South Coast Railway, William Stroudley designed B 1 0-4-2 tender express passenger locomotive number 176, *Pevensey*, constructed in 1890, here seen in full Stroudley improved Engine Green Livery, c1905. The B 1 0-4-2 tender passenger locomotives, were some of the most attractive and famous Brighton constructed locomotives of their time, there being thirty-six, in the class. The Gladstone class B 1 0-4-2 tender passenger locomotives represented some of the best in Victorian locomotive engineering during the mid-nineteenth century. Locomotive number 214 Gladstone constructed at Brighton works in 1882, was saved by the Stephenson Locomotive Society in 1927 and is preserved at the National Railway Museum, York. The class survived to be taken in to Southern stock in 1923, but were gradually withdrawn from the mid-1920s.

Chapter 8

Tractive Force and Adhesion

Two cylinders, of equal diameters, are universally employed in locomotives coupled to one axle, except, if we may, in the compound-cylinder locomotives designed by M. Mallet, recently introduced on the Bayonne and Biarritz Railway, in which the cylinders are of unequal diameters. But, taking the cylinders as of equal diameters, the pressure or tractive force at the rails, equivalent to the effective mean pressure developed in the cylinders, is given by the following simple formula, first, it is believed, propounded by Pambour:

$$T = \frac{d^2 \, Lp}{D}$$

Reversely, the effective mean pressure on the pistons, equivalent to a given tractive force at the rails, is expressed by the formula:

$$p = \frac{D \, T}{d^2 \, L}$$

d = the diameter of the cylinder, in inches.
L = the length of the stroke, in inches.
D = the diameter of the driving-wheel, in inches.
p = the effective mean pressure on the piston, in lbs per square inch.
T = the equivalent traction force at the rails, in lba.

That is to say: – *to find the Tractive Force* – multiply the square of the diameter of the pistons, in inches, by the length of the stroke, in inches, and by the effective mean pressure on the pistons, in lbs per square inch; and divide the product by the diameter of the driving-wheels, in inches. The quotient is the equivalent force, as tractive force, at the rails, in pounds.

To find the Effective Mean Pressure – Multiply the diameter of the driving-wheel, in inches, by the total equivalent tractive force at the rails, in pounds; and divide the product by the square of the diameter of the cylinders, in inches, and by the length of stroke in inches. The quotient is the effective mean pressure in lbs per square inch.

It is understood, of course, that so much of the power developed in the cylinders, as is necessary to overcome the resistance of the machinery of the engine, is intercepted and consumed; and that only the balance of the power is available for tractional action at the rails, and there exerted. But, for the sake of reducing, for purposes of estimation, all the resistances of the engine, as well as those of the train, to one standard for measurement, the whole of the steam-power in the cylinders, as measurable by the indicator, is reduced to an equivalent tractional force at the rail.

The proportion of the adhesion-weight, or driving-weight, of the engine, which measures the force of adhesion available as tractive force, is very variable: from one-fifth in dry weather – according to the writer's experiments on the adhesion upon railways – to one-ninth in damp weather, when the rails may be slippery. To keep within the limits of one-ninth in proportioning locomotives to this work would implicitly ensure the working of the engine in all states of the weather; but a larger fraction may wisely be assumed for the purposes of general estimates, particularly as the aid of dry sand dropped on the rails may be invoked, when necessary, for the increase of the adhesive force. A fraction of about one-sixth may be adopted.

Having adopted the fraction, about one-sixth of the load at the driving-wheels, or the driving-weight, as the force of adhesion for tractive effort, this effort can be readily calculated when the driving-weight is given. A ratio of one-sixth gives an adhesion of (2240/6 =) 373lbs per ton. A ration of 1 to 6.4 would give an adhesion of 350lbs per ton. A driving-weight of 10 tons would, on this last basis, give an adhesion of (350 x 10 =) 3500lbs; 20 tons weight would give 7000lbs; and 30 tons weight, 10,500lbs adhesion.

Section II: English Types of Locomotives

Since the power of the engine is brought into action through the adhesion or frictional hold of the driving-wheels upon the rails, it is necessary, for great powers, to couple together two pairs of wheels, or even three, or a greater number of pairs, by side-rods attached to cranks or crank-pins on the axles or the wheels, in order that the frictional hold of the other wheels may be brought into action to assist the first pair of driving-wheels, and to utilise and apply for traction-work the power of the engine developed in the cylinders. The coupling of the wheels leads to a great variety of arrangements for giving effect to the tractive force of the engine. Many of these are illustrated in *Railway Machinery*, diagram-plate 6, parts 1 and 2; also in an instructive paper on 'Distribution of Weight in Locomotives', by Mr John Robinson, read at the Institution of Mechanical Engineers in 1864; and in another paper by the same writer, 'On Modern Locomotives', read at the Institution of Civil Engineers in 1873. The selection of ten types, illustrated for general arrangement in Figs. 35 to 44, fairly represents the fundamental characteristics of English practice.

No. 1, the 'D. Luiz', is an express passenger-locomotive, which was constructed by Messrs. Beyer, Peacock, and Co, for the South-Eastern Railway of Portugal. The length of the base on which the engine rests on the rails – the wheel-base – is 15 feet 4 inches. The cylinders are inside, and are 16 inches in diameter, with a stroke of 22 inches. The driving-wheels are 7 feet in diameter. The area of fire-grate is 18 square feet, and the heating surface amounts to 1,339 square feet. The total weight of the engine in working order is 28 tons 6cwt, which is thus apportioned between the three pairs of wheels:

Leading-wheels	9 tons 4cwt
Driving-wheels	11 tons 12cwt
Trailing-wheels	<u>7 tons 10cwt</u>
	28 tons 6cwt

This locomotive and its tender are fully detailed and described in a following part of this book.

No. 2, 'The Lady of the Lake', is an express passenger-locomotive, one of a class which was designed by Mr John Ramsbottom with special regard to the running of express trains on the northern division of the

London and North-Western Railway. It has 16-inch cylinders, which are outside, with a stroke of 24 inches, and driving-wheels 7 feet 7½ inches in diameter, and stands on a wheel-base of 15 feet 5 inches in length. The fire-grate has an area of 14.9 square feet, and the heating surface is 1,098 square feet.

Total weight of Engine in working order	27 tons
Total weight of Tender in working order	17½ tons
Total weight of Engine and Tender in working order	44½ tons
Weight on Leading wheels of Engine	9 tons 8 cwt
Weight on Driving wheels of Engine	11 tons 10 cwt
Weight on Trailing wheels of Engine	6 tons 2 cwt
	27 tons 0 cwt
Weight of Engine empty	24 tons 10 cwt

This engine may be favourably contrasted with another express-engine, No. 373, constructed with inside cylinders, for the express service of the southern division of the London and North-Western Railway. It is a six-wheeled engine of maximum dimensions, and is indeed beyond the capacity of the English gauge of rails – 4 feet 8½ inches – for proper working. With cylinders of 18 inches in diameter, and a stroke of 24 inches, 7½ feet driving-wheels, and 26 square feet of fire-grate, it weighs 34¾ tons in working order, of which there are fully 14½ tons of driving-weight at one pair of wheels. With the tender, weighing 25 tons with fuel and water, the total mass to be moved amounts to about 60 tons, exclusive of train-weight. The boiler was designed for burning coal, with a combustion chamber within the barrel; but this chamber having been found insufficient for the purpose of mingling the combustible gases and consuming them before they reached the flue-tubes – which, indeed, was scarcely to be expected, the chamber being only 2 feet 8 inches in length – the fire-box was fitted with firebrick arches inside, and with deflecting-plates in the doorways. The grate is 7 feet long, in two parallel strips, separated by a mid-feather or water-partition, and the enormous amount of heating surface – 242½ square feet – has thus been attained in the fire-box and the combustion chamber, making what is called 'direct' heating surface, much more than was before attained on the narrow gauge. But the advantage of direct surface, or that which is exposed to the radiant heat of the fire, depends entirely upon its being within a reasonable distance from the fuel on the grate. Whereas, in this fire-box, the crown plates are 6 feet 3 inches above the grate; and, consequently, the upper portions of the surface are nearly inoperative for evaporation. The first concern should be to bring the surface near to the fire, or the fire near to the surface. It

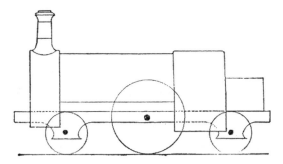

Figure 35. No. 1. 'D. Luiz'.

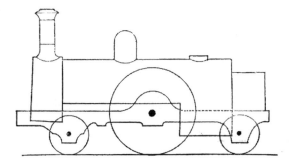

Figure 36. No. 2. 'The Lady of the Lake', London and North-Western Railway.

is thus that the efficient performance of Mr Cudworth's boiler, Fig. 39, with the elevated inclined grate, is to be accounted for, since in that boiler not only the lateral but the horizontal surface is thoroughly heated by direct action. The great extension of fire-box and combustion-chamber in No. 373, led to the curtailment of the flue-tubes to 9 feet 4 inches in length, and to the attempt to compensate for this by packing 214 of them together, at ½-inch distances apart, making 980 square feet of heating surface. Now, besides surface, circulation is wanted – the circulation of the water to, and the steam from amongst the tubes. The evaporative power of a less number of tubes, placed at ¾ inch apart, would have been decidedly greater than that of the tubes as they are.

Contrasting the 'Lady of the Lake' with No. 373, its weight, in the first place, is only 27 tons in working order, and the tender 17½ tons, making a total of 44½ tons, against 60 tons for No. 373. The fire-box is of the ordinary form, 4 feet 1½ inch long, and 3 feet 6 inches wide, with little more than half the grate-surface of No. 373, and it was fitted for coal-burning, with a brick arch, and two square air openings in front.[11] The

11. These openings are now removed.

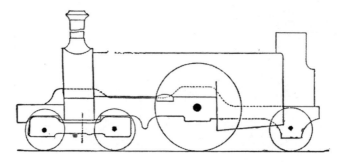

Figure 37. No. 3. Stirling's Express Locomotive, Great Northern Railway.

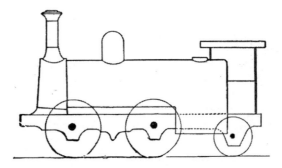

Figure 38. No. 4. Mixed Engine.

heating surface of the fire-box is little more than one-third of that of No. 373, but the crown-plates are nearly one foot nearer to the grate than in the other engine. There are fewer tubes – 192 of $1^7/8$ inch in diameter – but they are $5/8$ inch apart.

No. 373 has the advantage of the 'Lady', in the greater size of the blast-orifice, which is 5¼ inches for the former, and 4¼ inches for the latter, owing to the larger grate of No. 373, which does not require the same sharpness of blast to draw the air through. The proportions in question are here brought together for comparison:

	'Lady of the Lake' Sq ft	No. 373. Sq ft
Area of Fire-grate	15	26
Heating Surface of Fire-box	85	242½
Heating Surface of Tubes	1,013	980½
Heating Surface of Total	1,098	1,223
Driving-weight	11½ tons	14 tons
Diameter of Blast-Orifice	4¼ in.	5¼ in.

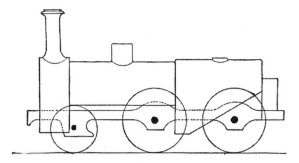

Figure 39. No. 5. Cudworth's Engine.

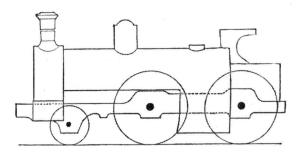

Figure 40. No. 6. Ramsbottom and Webb's Express Engine.

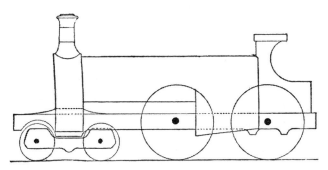

Figure 41. No. 7. Johnson's Express Engine.

The following are averaged results of the performances of engines of both of these classes in 1862–63.[12] The weights of the trains were averaged from actual observation, being 8½ tons per vehicle, with passengers and luggage. It appears that, whilst the southern engines had only 36 per cent,

---

12. Derived from the *Exhibited Machinery* of 1862; page 11.

more train-load, they consumed 55 per cent, more coal than the northern engines. The consumption per ton of gross weight, including the engine and tender, is at the rate of .26lb per ton per mile for the southern, and .23lb per ton per mile for the northern: – showing that there was no mechanical advantage in the southern boiler, with its extensive direct heating surface, over the northern boiler of the ordinary kind:

	'Lady of the Lake' Sq ft	No. 373. Sq ft
Gross Weight of Engine, Tender, and Train	117.35 tons	193–36 tons
Average Number of Vehicles	8.58	11.7
Average Weight of Train	72.93 tons	99.56 tons
Consumption of Coal:		
Per mile	26.77lbs	41.68lbs
Per ton of Train per mile	0.37lb	0.42lb
Per ton gross of Engine, Tender, and Train	0.23lb	0.26lb

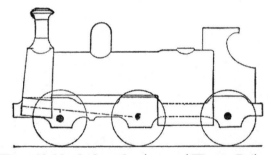

Figure 42. No. 8. Great Southern and Western Railway.

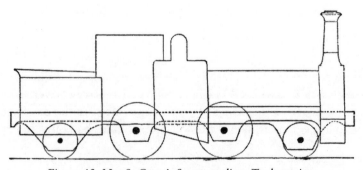

Figure 43. No. 9. Cross's Steep-gradient Tank-engine.

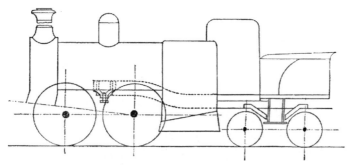

Figure 44. No. 10. Fairlie System. Great Southern and Western Railway.

The reversing gear of the 'Lady of the Lake' is worked by means of a screw and a hand-wheel, instead of the usual long lever and notched sector, than which it is much more easily worked, saving the engineman a great deal of fatigue. The tender of the engine is placed on six wheels: its weight, empty, 9½ tons; full, 17½ tons. It is fitted with Mr Ramsbottom's apparatus for picking up water whilst running, in which a scoop is let down from the bottom of the tender and dips into the water contained in a long open trough between the rails, from which it is scooped up into the tank while running. A minimum speed of 22 miles per hour is required for this operation. By the aid of the water-lifter, an express engine has been enabled to run the whole distance from Holyhead to London – 264 miles – in one continuous run, at an average speed of 42 miles per hour.

No. 3, an express locomotive of the Great Northern Railway, designed by Mr Patrick Stirling, is one of the most recent developments of the single-wheel engine. It is placed on eight wheels, of which the first four wheels are framed in a bogie, or truck, pivoted on a centre under the smoke-box. The cylinders are placed outside, and between the wheels of the bogie at each side. They are 18 inches in diameter, with a stroke of 28 inches: – dimensions which, taken together, exceed in magnitude those of any other engine for English passenger-traffic. The driving-wheels are 8 feet 1 inch in diameter, and the trailing-wheels are 4 feet 1 inch; the bogie-wheels are 3 feet 11 inches in diameter, and the axles are placed at a distance apart of 6½ feet between centres. The bogie is not pivoted centrally between the axles; the pivot is, on the contrary, placed 3 feet 6 inches behind the leading axle of the bogie, and is only 3 feet in front of the hind axle. The effect of this unequal distribution is to divide the load on the bogie, so that the less weight is on the leading bogie-axle and the greater weight on the hind bogie-axle, leading up by gradations to the maximum weight on the driving-wheels. In this way, the weight of the engine in working order, 39 tons, is so distributed:

Leading bogie-wheels	15 tons	7 tons
Hind bogie-wheels	15 tons	8 tons
Driving-wheels		16 tons
Hind-wheels		8 tons
Total Weight of Engine in working order		39 tons

As Mr Stirling intelligibly puts it, 'the bogies in front carry a comparatively light weight on each wheel, but quite sufficient to solidify the road before the driving wheels come on the rails, and thereby put the rails in the best position to carry the weight of the large wheels.' It may be added that the load at the hind-wheels also has its importance; it holds down the rails behind the drivers, as the load on the bogie-wheels does in front. Thus a long and comparatively steady bed is made for the engine. 'The engine,' Mr Stirling adds, 'seems to have plenty of adhesion for the size and power of the cylinders, and does not slip more than coupled engines under similar circumstances; and, with a slight application of dry sand, slipping is entirely prevented.' The weight – 15 tons – on the single pair of driving-wheels would be excessive, and would no doubt overtask the resistance of rails of iron. But the rails on the Great Northern Railway are of steel, and, as Mr Fowler says, 'Mr Stirling, with great judgment, has taken advantage of this altered condition of things, and has put 15 tons on the single driving-wheels of the Great Northern engines.'[13] The weight on the driving-wheels, it is stated, does not appear to be objectionably heavy. These large engines are the least fatiguing to the road.

The bogie-axles, it has been said, are 6½ feet apart, the distance from the pivot of the bogie to the driving-axle is 10 feet 9 inches, and from the driving-axle to the trailing-axle 8 feet 8 inches, making a total wheel-base of (3 feet 6 inches) + (10 feet 9 inches) + (8 feet 8 inches) = 22 feet 11 inches. Reckoned from the pivot of the bogie, the length of the wheel-base is 19 feet 5 inches.

There is another advantage derived from the backward position of the bogie-pivot: that the bogie leads better in having the leading-wheels better in advance, than if the pivot were equidistant between the axles. Not only do the leading-wheels turn to the curve with greater facility, but the hind bogie-wheels make less transversal movement towards the outer rail, and, in so much, the guiding of the engine is eased.

The engine is placed on two longitudinal frame-plates, 1¼ inch in thickness, one plate on each side, which carry inside bearings for the driving and the trailing axles; the boiler is made of Yorkshire plates,

---

13. Discussion on Mr J. Robinson's paper, in the *Proceedings of the Institution of Civil Engineers,* 1873–74; vol. xxxvii., page 23.

½ inch thick, and is telescopic; the plates are lap-jointed, double-riveted longitudinally, single-riveted circularly and vertically. The pressure in the boiler is 140lbs per square inch. The firebox is of copper; the tube-plate is ¾ inch thick, the back-plate ⁵/₈ inch, and the sides and the crown-plate ½ inch. The roof is stayed to the external shell by wrought-iron stays, ⁷/₈ inch in diameter, secured into the copper plates and into the shell nearly radial to the curves. The firebox contains a sloping mid-feather, projected from the tube-plate, below the tubes, and reaching more than halfway over to the doorway. It acts by deflecting the combustible gases towards the doorway, where air is admitted and directed by a deflecting-plate. There are 217 brass tubes, 1⁹/₁₆ inch in diameter externally; this diameter is exceptionally small, and whilst, by the comparatively minute subdivision of surface, heat may be more promptly abstracted, it is permitted to place the tubes at wider distances apart, and thus to facilitate circulation. The area of fire-grate is 17.6 square feet; the heating surface is, in the fire-box, 122 square feet, and, in the tubes, 1,043 square feet; total surface, 1,165 square feet, or 66 times the area of grate.

Mr Stirling, on the question of single wheels versus coupled wheels, states that he constructed two classes of engines for passenger-traffic – one class with four 6½-feet wheels coupled, the other with a single pair of 7-feet driving-wheels. The boilers of the two classes were alike; also the cylinders, which were 17 inches in diameter, with a stroke of 24 inches; the pressure in the boilers was 140lbs.

With like trains, the single-wheel engine had the best of it; in fact, it generally beat the coupled engine, in time, from King's Cross to Potter's Bar, a distance of nearly 13 miles, nearly all up-hill, the gradients varying from 1 in 105 for two miles, to 1 in 200. By these results he was led to believe that sufficient adhesion could be got with a single pair of driving-wheels, whilst there was no doubt of the superiority of a single engine, in freedom and economy, over a coupled engine. In designing the 8-feet wheel engine, Fig. 37, he determined to use a large wheel, being satisfied that the larger the wheels the greater the adhesion to the rails; and, as he could not employ inside cylinders, in consequence of the height of the cranks, he placed the cylinders outside, where he could get them between the wheels of the bogie, and in a horizontal line with the centre of the driving-wheel. Engines of this class travel between King's Cross and Leeds or York. The steepest gradients on the route are met with leaving Leeds, ascending 1 in 50, besides the gradient of 1 in 105 leaving King's Cross. The quickest curves have a radius of 15 chains; although the engines pass easily over curves of much shorter radius, at York station and elsewhere. Trains of from 16 to 22 carriages are taken from King's Cross Station with ease; and, on several occasions, 28 carriages have been taken, and time has been kept. On one occasion, a distance of 15 miles in twelve minutes was accomplished, with a train of 16 carriages; making a speed of 75 miles per hour. The engine had taken a train of 33 carriages, full of passengers, from Doncaster to Scarborough and back, at a speed of 45 miles per hour. It is capable of moving a gross weight of engine, tender, and train, 356 tons, on a level, at a speed of 45 miles per hour, with a working pressure of 140lbs. With trains averaging 16 carriages of from 10 to 12 tons each, the consumption of coal has been 27lbs per mile, including the fuel for getting up steam and piloting. The engines are employed on the heaviest and fastest passenger-train service, and it is stated that they excel all the other engines on the line, in capacity for work and in performance.

No. 4, the first example of a coupled-wheel locomotive, has the cylinders inside, and has four wheels coupled 'in front,' with a pair of trailing-wheels. It is known as a 'mixed engine'; that is to say, it is adapted for either passenger-traffic or goods-traffic – a generally useful type. In this engine, the cylinders are 16 inches in diameter, with a stroke of 22 inches; the coupled wheels are 5 feet in diameter. In an engine of this kind, the crank-axle should be placed well back, so that as much useful weight as is practicable may be placed upon the leading-axle, for the purpose of adhesion. The following is the distribution of the weight of the engine on the three axles:

Leading-axle	9.77 tons
Driving-axle	10.27 tons
	20.04 tons
Trailing-axle	4.42 tons
Total	24.46 tons

Here is an excellent distribution of weight for the purpose of the engine. The loads at the leading and the driving axles are nearly equal: – the near equality of loads being conducive to equality of wear of the wheel-tyres and to ease of working; at the same time that the load at the driving-axles is the greater, the excess being conducive to the prevention of incipient slipping at the driving-wheels which may take place when the bearings of the coupling rods are not taut. The wheel-base is 15 feet, in which the driving-axle is midway between the extreme axles. In such an engine, it is an essential condition that the cylinder should be elevated and inclined towards the driving-axle, so that the guide-bars and gearing should clear the leading-axle. The area of the grate is 15 square feet and the heating surface amounts to upwards of 1,000 square feet.

No. 5 is an equally useful class of engine, four-coupled 'behind,' for passenger traffic. It represents the style of engine designed by Mr J. J. Cudworth for service on the South-Eastern Railway; and, with its inclined fire-grate and sloping fire-box, it lends itself to an equable distribution of the weight on the axles. On a wheel-base of 15 feet, the weight of the engine, 30½ tons, in working order, is thus distributed:

Leading-wheels		9 tons 9cwt
Driving-wheels	10 tons 15cwt.	
Trailing-wheels	<u>10 tons 6cwt.</u>	
		<u>21 tons 1cwt.</u>
		30 tons 10cwt.

Here, by the circumstance that the fire-box is sloped upwards at the bottom, the hind-axle can be placed under the fire-box, and so considerably nearer to the centre of gravity,that it takes about as much weight as the driving-wheels to which it is coupled; whilst the leading-wheels are also so well loaded that the distribution of the weight of the engine is nearly equalised on the three axles. And, although the engine weighs upwards of 30 tons, the load on any axle does not amount to 11 tons, whilst more than two-thirds of the gross weight of the engine is placed upon the coupled wheels.

The cylinders are 16 inches in diameter, with a stroke of 24 inches, and the driving-wheels are 6 feet in diameter. The fire-box is 7 feet 6 inches long, and the grate is 7 feet long, having a short dead-plate at the upper end, and a clinker-plate for dropping the fire at the lower end, next the tube-plate. The fire-box is divided longitudinally into two parts by a water mid-feather, as before explained, page 73. The framing is double at each side, giving outside bearings to all the axles, and inside bearings, in addition, to the driving-axle.

This engine, No. 118, S. E. R., and other coal-burning engines similar in construction, consuming from 25lbs to 30lbs of coal per mile, with passenger trains, has evaporated 8.9lbs of water per pound of coal on the London and Maidstone trains. Another engine of the same kind, No. 142, with main-line trains, going at the rate of 31 miles per hour excluding stoppages, or 28.6 miles per hour including stoppages at 11 mile intervals, consumed 26lbs of a mixture of Hartley and coking coal per mile, evaporating 8.6lbs of water per pound of coal. The train consisted of an average of 13.2 carriages, and the gross total weight of engine, tender, and train was 116 tons. The fuel was consumed at the rate of .225lbs per ton gross per mile.

No. 6, like the preceding engine, is an express passenger-locomotive, having inside cylinders and four-coupled wheels behind, designed by

Mr John Ramsbottom for the London and North-Western Railway, modified in some of its details by his successor, Mr F. W. Webb. It differs from No. 5 in the form of the firebox, which is shorter, and is of the usual rectangular shape. The longitudinal frame-plates, single on each side, are 1 inch thick, giving inside bearings to all the axles. The cylinders are 17 inches in diameter, with 24 inches of stroke; the driving-wheels are 6 feet 7½ inches in diameter, and the leading-wheels 3 feet 7½ inches. The coupled axles are 8 feet 3 inches apart between centres, and the leading-axle is 7 feet 5 inches in advance of the driving-axle, making a wheel-base of 15 feet 8 inches.

The driving-axle, it may be observed, is placed well forward; the centre of the axle is about 2 feet 7 inches in advance of the fire-box shell; and that this considerable advance should have been effected without disadvantageously shortening the connecting-rod, this rod is forked so as to gain in length. The rod is, in fact, about 5 feet 10 inches in length, making it nearly six times (exactly 5.83 times) the length of the crank. The object of the great advancement of the dividing axle and wheels has been to deliver as great a weight as was practicable upon the trailing-wheels for adhesion. For contrast, it may here be noted that in Mr Stirling's engine, in which there was no necessity for specially making provision of trailing weight, the driving-axle is not more than 1 foot 9 inches in advance of the fire-box shell; the connecting-rod is about 6 feet 10 inches in length, nearly six times (exactly 5.86 times) the length of the crank. Thus, it appears that, in this engine, having 4 inches longer stroke, the connecting-rod is fully as long proportionally as in the coupled engine under notice.

The weight of the engine in working order, No. 6, Fig. 40, is 29 tons 4cwt, thus distributed:

Leading-wheels		9 tons 9cwt
Driving-wheels	19 tons 15 cwt	11 tons 0cwt
Trailing-wheels	19 tons 15 cwt	8 tons 15cwt
Total		29 tons 4cwt

Thus, the driving weight is two-thirds of the total weight. But it is apparent that, by reason of the necessity for placing the hind-axle behind the fire-box, the driving weight is more unequally distributed than in No. 5.

The boiler is of Lowmoor plates, $^1/_3 {}^3/_2$ inch thick, lap-jointed, with the working pressure 120lbs per square inch. The fire-box is about 4 feet 3 inches long and 3½ feet wide, making an area of fire-grate 15 square feet. The fire-box contains a brick arch, reaching from the tube-plate a little more than half-way towards the fire-box. Under the arch, there are two circular holes, 7 inches in diameter, for the admission of air through the front of the fire-box, covered by valves or dampers which can be worked from the foot-plate. A pair of sliding fire-doors are adapted with connections for being moved simultaneously, such as will be described and illustrated for the 'D. Luiz' engine. There are 192 brass flue-tubes, $1^7/_8$ inch in diameter. The heating surface of the tubes is 1,013 square feet, and that of the fire-box is 89 square feet; together, 1,102 square feet, which is 73½ times the grate-area.

The engine can move a gross weight of 293 tons, comprising engine, tender, and train, on a level, at a speed of 45 miles per hour, with a working pressure of 120lbs in the boiler. With trains averaging 10 carriages, the consumption of coal is 26.3lbs per mile.

No. 7 is an express passenger-locomotive, designed by Mr S. W. Johnson for the traffic of the Midland Railway. It is a development of the four-coupled passenger engine, with inside cylinders, into an eight-wheel bogie engine: the bogie in front, the coupled wheels behind. The driving-axle has been placed as near as possible to the fire-box shell, which is 21 inches from the centre of the axle: just sufficient to clear the cranks and the connecting-rods. The trailing-axle is also placed near the fire-box shell; they are 10 inches apart. By such a disposition, the driving weight is, as nearly as practicable, equally distributed on the two axles, whilst the fixed wheel-base is restricted to a length of 8 feet 6 inches. The comparatively great overhang of the fore end of the engine – overhung, that is to say, in advance of the driving-axle – which would have been too great, and would have excessively loaded a single leading-axle, is, on the contrary, not more than sufficient for the two axles of the bogie, and for clearing the way for the driving-wheels. The centre of the bogie is, in fact, placed just under the cylinders, 10 feet in advance of the driving-axle; making a total wheel-base of 18 feet 6 inches from the centre of the bogie to the trailing-axle. The axles of the bogie, which is on Mr William Adams's system, are 6 feet apart between centres, and tha total wheel-base upon which the engine is supported is equal to (6 feet + 7 feet) + (8 feet 6 inches) = 21 feet 6 inches.

The cylinders are 18 inches in diameter, with a stroke of 26 inches; the driving-wheels are 7 feet in diameter, and the bogie-wheels are 3 feet 6 inches. The heating surface of the fire-box is 110 square feet, and that of the tubes is 1,203 square feet; making together 1,313 square feet, which is 75 times the grate-area, 17½ square feet.

The total weight of the engine empty, and in working order, is distributed thus:

	Empty			In working order		
	t.	c.	q.	t.	c.	q.
Leading (Bogie)	13	8	1	14	2	3
Driving-wheels	12	11	1	14	8	3
Trailing-wheels	13	0	0	13	9	3
Total weight	38	19	2	42	1	1

	t.	c.
The weight of the tender (six-wheeled), empty is	17	17
The weight of the tender in average working order	25	10
Capacity of tank	2950 gallons.	
Capacity for coal	3½ tons.	

The total weight of the engine and tender together, in working order, is 67 tons 11¼cwt. They are fitted with continuous brakes, which are applied to the driving and the trailing wheels of the engine, and to all the wheels of the tender.

The average load taken by engines of this class is 14 carriages, at the timebill speed of about 50 miles per hour; and up several gradients of from 1 in 120 to 1 in 130, with a consumption of 28lbs of Derbyshire coal per mile. The engines can take, as a maximum load, 17 carriages between Manchester and Derby, both ways, over ruling gradients of 1 in 90 and 1 in 100, for 10 miles, and at a speed up the banks of 35 miles per hour; and on a level, or on falling gradients, at 50 miles per hour. The curves on the Manchester line are very frequent; they vary from 11 chains to 40 chains radius.

Average weight of train (14 carriages) including passengers	154 tons
Enging and tender, in working order	67 tons
	221 tons

Average weight of train (17 carriages) including passengers	187 tons
Enging and tender, in working order	67 tons
	254 tons

No. 8, made for the Great Southern and Western Railway of Ireland, represents the usual form of six-coupled goods-engines used in England. It is made with two single frame-plates, one on each side, 1 inch thick. The cylinders are inside, and are 17 inches in diameter, with a stroke of 24 inches. The six wheels are 5 feet 1¼ inch in diameter, and are placed on a base 15 feet 6 inches in length; in which the leading and driving axles are 7 feet 3 inches apart, and the driving and trailing axles are 8 feet 3 inches apart. Here, as in the engine four-coupled behind, it is in the interest of the equality of distribution of the weight, to place the driving-axle well forward. It has been placed so far forward, in this instance, that the length of the connecting-rod has only been made about 5 feet 7 inches, which is little over 5½ times the length of the crank. Even so, the weight on the hind-wheels is considerably less than on the others:

	Tons	cwt	qrs
Leading-wheels	10	12	1
Driving-wheels	11	6	3
Trailing-wheels	8	15	2
Total weight in working order	30	14	2

The boiler is of Yorkshire iron plates, ½ inch thick; the fire-box is of ½ inch copper plates. There are 160 brass tubes, 2 inches in diameter. The grate area is 17.5 square feet. The heating surface in the fire-box is 93 square feet, and in the tubes 846 square feet; total, 939 square feet, equal to 53 6 times the grate area.

The engine draws a gross weight – engine, tender, and train – of 607 tons on a level at a speed of 25 miles per hour, with a working pressure of 140lbs per square inch in the boiler. The average consumption of coal is 35lbs per mile with a load of 55 waggons.

No. 9 is a steep-gradient tank-locomotive, designed by Mr James Cross for the St. Helen's Railway. The supply of fuel and water is carried upon the engine itself; and hence it is called a tank-locomotive or tank-engine.

This engine was designed to obviate the acknowledged evils of a long rigid wheel-base, particularly for the ascent of steep inclines in combination with sharp curves; and for this object it was constructed with the radial axle-boxes and spring-tyres invented by Mr W. B. Adams. The engine is placed on eight wheels, of which the four central wheels are coupled, and each extreme pair is fitted so as to radiate to curves. The driving and the coupled axles are placed respectively in front and behind the fire-box, 8 feet apart, and the leading and trailing axles are placed each at 7 feet from the coupled axles, or at an extreme distance of 22 feet apart, and are fitted with radial axle-boxes, which are formed in segments of circles, and are free to traverse laterally and radially between the guides fixed on the frame. Steel tyres are applied to all the wheels, with springs between the tyre and the rim.

By the radiating movement of the extreme axles, according to which they become inclined more and more to the coupled axles, as the curve becomes quicker, these axles are maintained constantly at right angles or radial to the curve.

The radial axle-boxes are only a little larger than ordinary engine axle-boxes; but, instead of being square to the framing, they are struck with a radius which has its centre in the centre of the adjoining axle, giving, in this case, a radius of 7 feet, to fit -which the axle-box guide-blocks are curved. The boxes are allowed to play laterally by 4½ inches on each side; and the spring-pins, instead of being fixed immediately on the top of the boxes, are each fitted with a small slide or roller, so as to allow the boxes to traverse freely.

The fixed rectangular wheel-base is, therefore, limited to that of the coupled wheels, which is 8 feet. This 8-feet rigid base, again, is eased in passing round curves by the use of the spring-tyres, which, it appears, admit of a slight lateral movement.

It appeared that these tyres gave a better grip on the rail than ordinary rigid tyres. The augmentation of grip has been attributed to a slight flattening of the tyres under the weight of the engine, so presenting more surface for adhesion. The total weight of the engine in working order is 40¾ tons, thus distributed:

Leading-wheels			7 tons 15cwt
Driving-wheels		11 tons 15cwt	
Coupled-wheels		11 tons 5cwt	
			23 tons 0cwt
Trailing-wheels:	Empty	4 tons 10cwt	
	Water	4 tons 5cwt	
	Fuel	1 ton 5cwt	
			10 tons 0cwt
Total weight			40 tons 15cwt

The driving or adhesion weight is 58 per cent, of the total weight. But, regarding the hind-wheels with the tank, as a single-axle tender attached to the engine proper, the weight of the latter would be taken as 30¾ tons, and the adhesion-weight would be 75 per cent, of the weight of the engine proper.

The cylinders are 15 inches in diameter, with a stroke of 20 inches. The driving-wheels are 5 feet 1 inch in diameter, and the carrying-wheels are 4 feet 2 inches. The fire-grate has an area of 16¼ square feet; and there are 687 square feet of heating surface, equal to 42.3 times the grate-area.

'This engine', says Mr Cross,[14] 'was completed in the first week of November 1863, and has been [26 April 1864] since running regularly,

---

14. See his paper on 'Locomotive Engines for Ascending Steep inclines in conjunction with Sharp Curves', in the *Proceedings of the Institution of Civil Engineers*, 1863–64; vol. xxiii., page 406.

taking its turn of duty regularly with passenger-trains or coal-trains, or as a shunting engine, and about the numerous works connected by sharp curves -with the St. Helen's line. The motion round curves is free from all jerking, and on straight lines the speed is more than 60 miles an hour, either end of the engine being first, without any train behind to give steadiness; and the motion is so smooth, that it has only been by taking the actual time that the engineers have convinced themselves of the fact of the speed exceeding 40 miles an hour. It was built to traverse curves of 200 feet radius. This it does with the greatest facility. It has regularly worked the passenger-trains round a curve of 1000 feet radius, going directly off the straight line by a pair of facing points, at a speed of more than 30 miles an hour; and it has gone round a curve of 132 feet radius.

'It has also drawn a train of twelve passenger-carriages, weighted up to 100 tons, exclusive of its own weight, at 60 miles an hour on the level. On a wet, slippery day, the engine started, and drew this load upon a gradient of 1 in 70; and it took seven carriages, making a load of 72¼ tons, up 1 in 36, on a curve of 440 feet radius. It has also drawn coal-trains of 250 tons over long gradients of 1 in 200 with the greatest ease.'

No. 10 is a double bogie-tank locomotive, on the system of Mr Bobert F. Fairlie. It was designed and constructed by Mr A. A. M'Donnell for the Great Southern and Western Railway. On Mr Eairlie's system, the engine is placed on two bogies, which may each have four wheels, or six, or any greater number. To each bogie, or it may be to one bogie only, a pair of steam-cylinders is fixed and connected to drive the bogie-wheels, which are coupled. As each bogie is swivelled independently to the boiler or to the frame, the engine is free to pass over any curve that can be taken by a truck having the wheel-base of the bogies, and, in so far, the engine may with equal facility pass along curves of any radius.

The annexed figure 45 illustrates the Fairlie engines, made with double boilers and double steam-bogies, for the Dunedin and Port Chalmers Railway, New Zealand. There are four 10-inch cylinders, with 18-inch stroke, and eight wheels 3 feet 9 inches in diameter, all coupled. The total heating surface amounts to 829 square feet. The tanks hold 800 gallons, and the coal-bunkers 17cwt. The weight, in working order, is 26 tons. It is reported that one of these engines, in unfavourable weather, hauled a train of 26 loaded waggons, carrying 7 tons each, up inclines of 1 in 56, where the train occupied two or three curves of 8½ chains radius.

The 'Little Wonder', a double steam-bogie engine, was constructed for the Festiniog Railway, a line in Wales, made to a gauge of 1 foot 11½ inches, or to what is known in round numbers as the 2-feet gauge. The boiler is double, having two fire-boxes united back to back with two distinct barrels and sets of flue-tubes, and, consequently, a chimney at

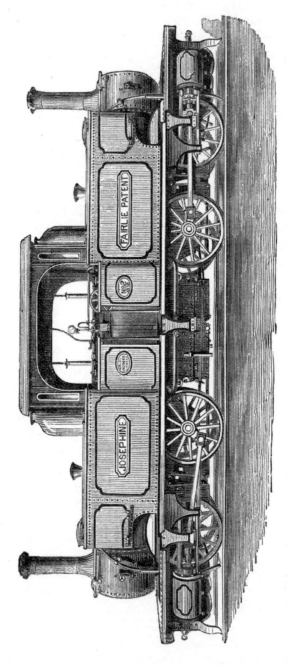

Figure 45. Double-Boiler Bogie Fairlie Engine, 3 feet 6 inch gauge. For the Dunedin and Port Chalmers Railway, New Zealand.

each end. A bogie is placed under each barrel, and each bogie has two pairs of wheels, coupled, worked independently by a pair of cylinders to each bogie. Thus a total wheel-base of 19 feet 1 inch in length is covered by the bogies, whilst each bogie has only a wheel-base of 5 feet, and the distance between the centres of the bogies is 14 feet 1 inch. The cylinders, four in number, are $8^{3}/_{16}$ inches in diameter, and have a stroke of 13 inches. The wheels are 2 feet 4 inches in diameter. The combined area of grate is 11 square feet, and the heating surface is 730 square feet, or 66½ times the grate-area. The weight of the engine in working order is 19½ tons. The capacity of the tanks is 800 gallons; the bunkers hold 20cwt of coal.

From the results of a series of well-attested trials of the 'Little Wonder', made in February, 1870, on the Festiniog Railway, the following may be selected for example. The engine left Portmadoc with a train of 72 waggons, 648 feet in length, as follows:

	Tons	cwt	qrs
Loaded Waggons (Slate Trucks)	138	17	2
Empty Waggons	43	13	0
Passengers	4	0	0
Train weight	186	10	2
Engine weight	19	10	0
Gross weight of Engine and Train	206	0	2

The engine started with steam of 170lbs per square inch, and it drew the train up a gradient of 1 in 85 at a speed of 5 miles per hour. The train, when it was started, stood partly on a curve of 4½ chains radius, and partly on a reverse curve of 8 chains radius. The weather was fine, with a strong, cold head-wind. The rails weighed 30lbs per yard, and were not fished.

Mr C. E. Spooner, the engineer and manager of the railway, states that the engine drew a train up the line, 80 tons weight, at a speed of 16 miles per hour, consuming 24.8lbs of coal per mile, for 13½ miles of incline. The fuel consumed for the up and down trips, taken together, was 14½lbs per mile. The average comparative performances of another engine of the same class, the 'James Spooner', and of a four-wheel coupled engine, were as follows:

	Double-bogie.	Ordinary.
Average load from Portmadoc and Miniord Junction to Daffros	67 tons	34 tons
Average weight of Coal consumed per Train	16cwt	10cwt
Coal per ton per mile	1.005lb	1.260lb

Turning to the Fairlie engine of Mr M'Donnell, Fig. 44, it differs from the 'Little Wonder' and other engines on Mr Fairlie's system, in having only one steam-bogie, the other bogie being without cylinders. The two bogies are connected by a carrying-frame which supports the boiler, as in all Mr Fairlie's later engines. The second bogie is arranged on the system of Mr William Adams. The cast-iron bearing-plate, through which the engine rests on the bogie, is stiffened with flanges on its lower side, which are expanded into a circular bearing surface, between which and the frame of the bogie a massive ring of indiarubber is interposed to carry the weight. This ring is confined between two discs of cast-iron with ledges, the upper one of which is secured to the bearing-plate, and is formed with a pivot which passes through the india-rubber ring, and descends into an eye formed in the lower disc – this disc resting on a cast-iron sliding-block, which is capable of lateral transverse movement to the extent of 2 inches each way from the centre line, between two transverse members of the bogie-frame. The whole is loosely connected together by a central bolt, which passes down through the pivot, with a washer-plate and nut below. With such means of free universal movement, the bogie is enabled to adapt itself to any curvature or inequality of the road. The eliding-block, it should be added, traverses the bogie on level surfaces, and is in this respect distinguished from the slides of the Bissell system, which ascend inclined planes in moving laterally; but the lateral movement is kept in check by auxiliary indiarubber springs which are opposed to it, and by means of which the bogie is restored to the central line of the engine, when the engine arrives on a straight portion of the road.

The pivot of the leading or steam bogie is formed with a flat face, to rest upon the socket, with lateral indiarubber check-springs to regulate the traverse, as in the other bogie. Any tendency to pitch on the part of the leading-bogie is checked by indiarubber springs fixed in front of the fire-box. The bearing-springs of the leading-bogie are connected by compensating beams; and, for the second bogie, a single spring is applied at each side, and spans the two axles.

The engine is found to run with a great degree of steadiness, and it passes round curves of 300 feet radius with ease. It can pass round a curve of 200 feet radius, but, then, the driving-wheels almost touch the carrying-frame.

The cylinders (one pair) are 15 inches in diameter, with a stroke of 20 inches; the wheels are 5 feet 7½ inches high. The wheel-base of the leading-bogie is 6 feet; and that of the trailing-bogie is 5 feet. The centres of the bogies are 14 feet 7 inches apart; and the total base covered by wheels amounts to 25 feet 7 inches. The capacity of the water-tank is 800 gallons; and that of the coal-boxes is good for 30cwt of coal. The weight in working order is 35 tons 17cwt, distributed thus:

Leading-bogie	22 tons	0cwt
Trailing-bogie	13 tons	17cwt
	35 tons	17cwt

from which it appears that the adhesion-weight is 61 per cent, of the total weight of the engine. With an average load of seven six-wheeled carriages, the engines of this construction, on the Great Southern and Western lines, have consumed an average of 20½lbs of coal per mile.

Wherever the Fairlie engines have been established at regular work, it has been demonstrated that they consume a considerably less proportion of fuel in performing equal work than ordinary engines made with fixed parallel axles. It further appears, from the most authoritative accounts, that the cost for repair is correspondingly less.

Section III:
Special Description of a Modern Locomotive

Chapter 9

General View of the Engine

The locomotive engine that has been selected for special description, as an example of modern design and construction, is the 'D. Luiz', an express passenger-engine which was constructed for the South-Eastern Railway of Portugal, by Messrs. Beyer, Peacock, and Co, Manchester. This engine, illustrated by Pigs. 46 to 52, is a type of the prevalent style of English inside-cylinder express locomotive, with single wheels. The railways of Portugal, like those of Spain, are constructed to a gauge of 5 feet 5¾ inches between the rails – usually known, in round numbers, as the 5 feet 6 inch gauge. This gauge is about 9½ inches wider than the English national gauge of 4 feet 8½ inches, and so affords additional facilities for the disposal and proportioning of the machinery within and about the framing and wheels of the engine. The cylinders are inside; the driving-wheels with their axle are placed in front of the fire-box; the leading-wheels and axle are behind the cylinders; and the trailing-wheels and axle are behind the fire-box. There is altogether 25½ tons of material employed in the construction of the engine – more than three times as much material as there was used in the making of the 'Planet', thirty years earlier. This weight is augmented by that of the water required to fill the boiler, and the fuel in the fire-box, which is about 2 tons 16cwt more: making in all 28 tons 6cwt, the weight of the engine in working order. The length of wheel-base upon which the load is supported is 15 feet 4 inches, in which the driving-wheels are placed mid-way between the leading-wheels and the trailing-wheels. This weight is distributed amongst the wheels, so as to dispose the greater proportion upon the driving-wheels; – or, exactly speaking, upon the rails under the driving-wheels. The adjustment of the weight is conveniently effected by means of the screws and nuts on which the bearing-springs over the driving-wheels are brought to bear upon the frame; and for working-duty the gross weight of the engine is distributed in the following proportions:

D. Luiz: Distribution of weight in Working Order.

Leading-wheels	9 tons	4cwt
Driving-wheels	11 tons	12cwt
Trailing-wheels	7 tons	10cwt
Total Weight	28 tons	6cwt

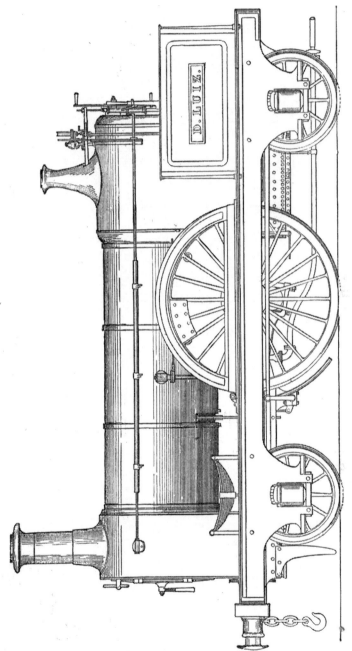

Figure 46. Express Passenger Locomotive, constructed by Messrs. Beyer, Peacock, and Co

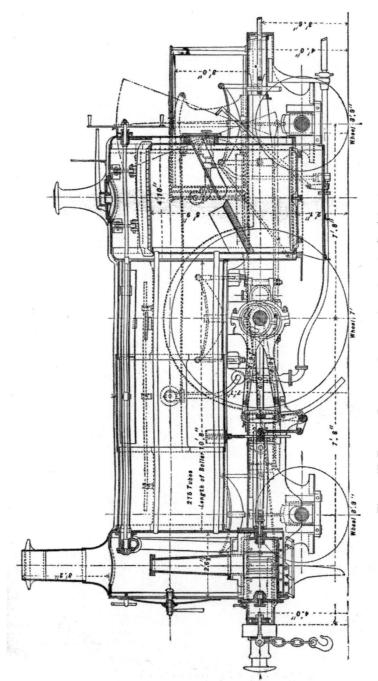

Figure 47. Express Passenger Locomotive – Longitudinal Section.

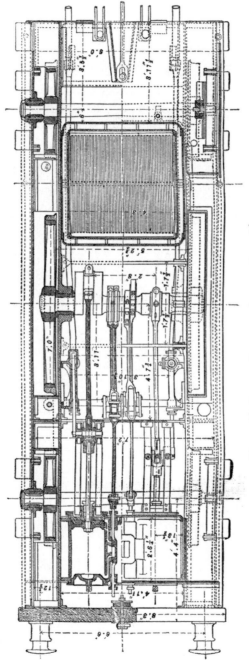

Figure 48. Express Passenger Locomotive – Plan.

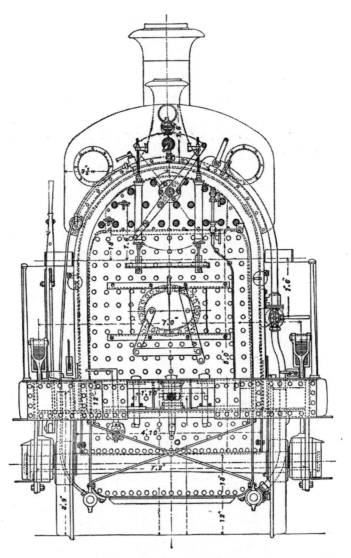

Figure 49. Express Passenger Locomotive – End elevation, at Fire-box.

From these data, the position of the centre of gravity of the engine, longitudinally, is readily calculated by means of the formula:

$$x = \frac{(D \times n) - (E \times m)}{W}$$

in which W is the gross weight, D and E are the loads at the leading-wheels and the trailing-wheels respectively, n and m are their horizontal distances

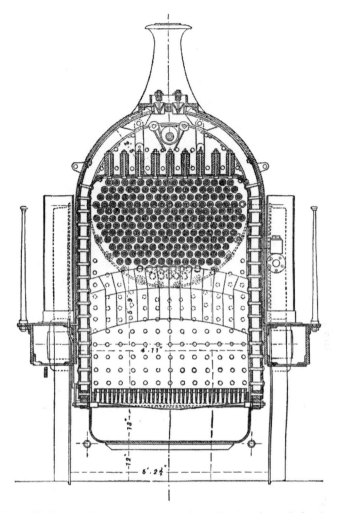

Figure 50. Express Passenger Locomotive – Section through fire-box.

from the driving-axle, and x is the distance of the centre of gravity from the driving-axle. As the moment (D x n) = (9.2 tons x $7^2/_3$ feet =) 69.5, and the moment (E x m) – (7.5 tons x $7^2/_3$ feet =) 57.5; then

$$x = \frac{69.5 - 57.5}{28.3} = .425 \text{ foot, or 5 inches;}$$

that is to say, the centre of gravity is 5 inches horizontally in advance of the centre of the driving-axle. It is on the side of the leading-axle, because the moment at the leading-axle is greater than that at the trailing-axle.

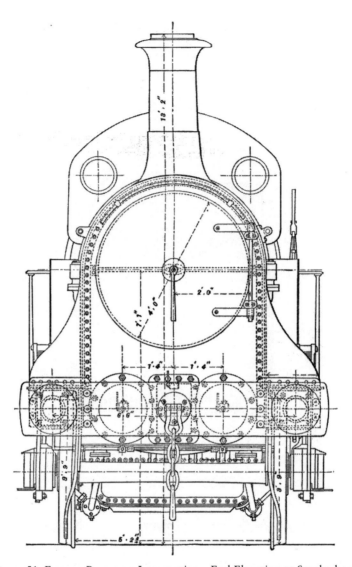

Figure 51. Express Passenger Locomotive – End Elevation at Smoke-box.

The upper edges of the side frame-plates are 4 feet above the level of the rails. The centre-line of the barrel of the boiler stands 7 feet 1 inch above the level of the rails, and the chimney reaches to a height of 13 feet 2 inches above the rails.

The working pressure of steam in the boiler is 120lbs per square inch.

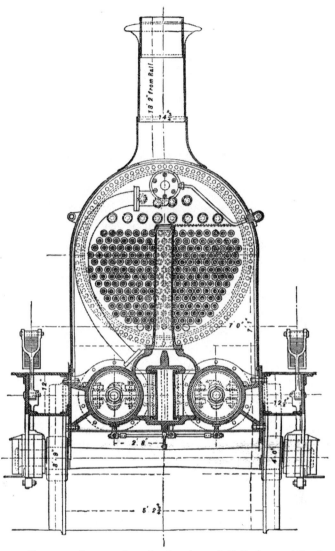

Figure 52. Express Passenger Locomotive – Section through Cylinders and Smoke-box.

Chapter 10

Framing

The general arrangement of the frame is shown in the plan, Fig. 48. It consists, fundamentally, of two pairs of longitudinal bars or slabs of wrought iron running straight from end to end, one pair at each side of the engine. The broad and comprehensive slab frame-plate here noticeable was introduced by Mr Beyer at a very early date in the history of the locomotive; and it is generally adopted in English and in Continental practice. These slabs are each 23 feet 1 inch in length, and are of massive scantling, being 1 inch in thickness, and having a ruling depth of 12 inches. They are, of course, made of greater depth where the cylinders are fixed to them, and the axle-guards are formed; and the inner plates are thickened up at the driving-axle, so as to form solid-forged guides for the axle-boxes. The guides for the other axles, which are merely carrying-axles, are applied to the outer plates, and are not forged solid with them, but are bolted on. Evidently, it is of the first importance that the place where the frame receives the first impulse of the steam-power – at the driving-axle – should be solidly constructed. The value of a solid frame-bearing to take the first of the stress of the steam was appreciated even in the early six-wheel engine of Stephenson, in which the guides for the axle-boxes were forged solid on the inside frame-plates, as in Figs. 20, page 37.

The four longitudinal frame-plates are, of course, strongly connected by transverse plates, and also by other means. First in importance are the steam-cylinders, as a bond of union, forming a stay extending 30¼ inches along each inside plate. The length of attachment is of the more importance, seeing that the inner plates are 4 feet 11 inches apart; it amounts to half the width apart, and affords great support for resisting diagonal strains. At the same end, each outer plate is bound to the inner plate by webs or gusset-plates and angle-irons, all riveted together. The same method of connection is adopted at the other end of the frame, next the foot-plate, and also at the sides of the fire-box. Again, the foot-plate forms, in connection with the draw-plate, a very strong fastening, the former reaching over all the four side plates, and the latter between the two inner plates – all riveted toge.ther with angle-irons. That these may be of length sufficient for a draw-plate of sufficient width and strength, the platform supported by the side plates extends to a length of 3 feet 11½ inches behind the fire-box, and 3 feet 6 inches behind the centre of the trailing-axle. Thus, a draw-plate is provided for, 2 feet 6 inches in width, or, like the length of the cylinders, half the width apart of the inside plates. The longitudinal, or side, plates are bound together also by transverse plates placed vertically. There is one, ½-inch thick, at the extreme end, embracing all the four plates. At the front end, each pair of plates is tied by a short ½-inch plate, and all the plates are efficiently connected by the buffer-beam of hard-wood, 6 inches thick and 16½ inches deep. The buffer-beam, of a comparatively accommodating material, supplies the most suitable means of binding together the fore-ends of the frame-plates – seeing that the cylinder-stays come up to within 13 inches of the beam. The transverse motion-plate, ¾-inch thick, which comes in half-way between the cylinders and the driving-axle, is useful in stiffening the long extent of frame between these parts; it is, indeed, essential for enabling the inside frame-plates to sustain, without buckling or tremor, the stress of the steam between the cylinders and the driving-axle, through a distance of nearly 8½ feet. The motion-plate itself is thoroughly stiffened by the four pairs of guide-bars which proceed from the cylinders, and are bolted to it, and by its attachment to the barrel of the boiler overhead. Then there is a pair of stay-bars inserted between the axle-guards of the inside plates, fore and aft of the axle. These bars perform the duty of giving a bearing to the links by which the springs for the driving-axle are connected to the frame; and they obviate the lateral twist which would result from the pull of the spring-links if they were attached direct to the frame-plates at the sides.

Finally, each pair of plates is covered by a platform or foot-plate, from one end to the other, riveted to them by angle-iron.

From this description, it must appear that the frame is so constructed as to combine the maximum of strength with the minimum of material. The cellular system is applied to good purpose. The total length of the frame, including the end transverse plates, is 23 feet 2 inches; the width, over the outside plates, is 7 feet 4 inches; and over the foot-plates 8 feet.

In the disposition of the frame and wheels as a carriage, it is notable that the driving-axle is made with only two bearings, which are inside the wheels, one bearing being close to each wheel; and that the leading and the trailing axles have their bearings outside the wheels. This is an arrangement which was originated by the late Mr John Gray; and it is now commonly adopted for its simplicity and convenience, and for the greater firmness of the frame, and the increased duration of the crank-axle – when compared with the earlier frames. In the Stephenson locomotive, pages 14 and 59, there were five bearings for the crank-axle. Mr Gray reduced the number to two, by removing the two outside bearings and the middle bearing; a modification which was warranted by the simplicity and directness of stress which it introduced, as well as by the simplification of detail. The steam-stress is, in fact, confined to the two inside frame-plates, and to the inside bearings of the crank-axle, close to the cranks.

The carrying-wheels, leading and trailing, are 3 feet 9 inches in diameter, and the driving-wheels are 7 feet. It has been thought that the carrying-wheels might with advantage have been larger, and no doubt there is room in the engine for enlarging them; but, if made larger, they would have departed from uniformity with the wheels of the tender, and they would have involved the breaking-up of the level foot-plates to provide a sufficient degree of clearance for them.

The guides for the driving-axle-box are shown in the plan, Fig. 48, forged solid on the inner frame-plates, together with the driving-axle-box, in its place between the guides, shown in detail in Figs. 53 and 54. The normal thickness of each frame-plate is 1 inch; for a length of 23 inches on each side of the centre of the axle, the frame is thickened to 1¼ inch of thickness, and is also heightened to the extent of 9½ inches above the normal level. Thus prepared, the large opening required to be made in the plate to receive the axle-box may be made without radically weakening it. The plate is made, on the contrary, absolutely stronger here than elsewhere by the accumulation of the forged mass around the opening, made up to a thickness of 6¾ inches, to afford a bearing, as a guide, for the axle-box at each side. The width of the face of each 'cheek' is 2¾ inches, and it is swept down gradually to the 1¼ inch of thickness already mentioned. The forging is carried, at the same thickness, 6¾ inches, over the opening for a depth of 7 inches, thus doing much more than preserving the continuity of the frame, for here there is a solid section, except where the spring-pin passes down, of (6¾ x 7 =) 47¼ square inches, whilst the frame, at its normal section, contains only (12 x 1 =) 12 square inches of area. True, the depth over the opening is only 7 inches against 12 inches, the normal depth; and in this locality the frame would be comparatively weak, as against vertical stress, but for the very powerful strut and 2-inch tie-bolt applied at the lower ends of the guides, by which the guides are thoroughly bound and framed as one piece. The vertical strength of the frame at the axle-box is, therefore, really that due to its whole depth. It is further to be observed that the load, through the spring, is applied at two points, which are 3 feet 3 inches apart, a distance that is equal to the span of the bearing-springs; and that, therefore, there is really no direct vertical stress upon the frame over the axle-box. The great demand upon its power of resistance is made for overcoming the lateral transverse stress which arises from the blows of the rails upon the driving-wheels, and

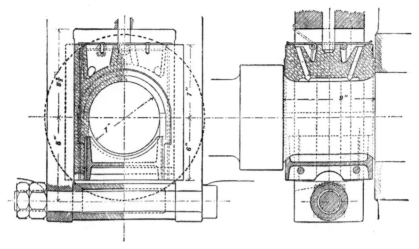

Figure 53. Driving-axle and part of   Figure 54. Driving-axle-box, and
Frame.   Crank-axle.

the strain in passing along curved portions of the line. For this purpose, the frame-plates are well fortified at the axle-boxes; and whilst there is, at the same time, a free length of more than 7 feet between the fixings before and behind the driving-wheel, on which a slight degree of lateral elastic action is permissible, even this lateral freedom is controlled by the two cross-bars, which extend between and bind together the two inside frame-plates at the points where the spring-links are attached.

Chapter 11

The Axle-Boxes

The axle-box for the driving-axle is shown in its place in Figs. 53 and 54. It is formed, in general outline, as a cubical block, with two exterior flat faces to take a bearing upon the parallel guides of the frame-plate; and it is bored out internally to receive the axle and to rest upon it. The axle-box is in two pieces. The upper part, of gun-metal, consists of the crown, which bears upon the axle, and the two sides, by which the axle is embraced, and by which the box takes its bearing on the guides. The surface of available contact between the brass and the axle is limited to something a little less than a semicircle. If it were originally bored out to the exact radius of the axle, it would lap the axle so closely that, when the engine is newly started, complete lubrication might be prevented, and the metals would heat and seize each other. To obviate such a contingency, the brass is bored out to a radius which is $1/32$ inch more than the radius of the axle, or to a diameter of $7^1/_{16}$ inches, the diameter of the axle being 7 inches. By such a simple provision, it is made impossible for the brass, when new, to seize the axle; and plenty of time is allowed for the lubrication to be perfected, and for the brass and the axle to accommodate themselves one to the other, and by degrees to come to true bearings. The length of the axle-box is, for a similar reason, a little shorter than the journal or bearing of the axle on which it rests; it is $8^{15}/_{16}$ inches long, whilst the journal is 9 inches long, making a difference of $1/_{16}$ inch as slackness or play between the journal and the brass. Again, there is an element of freedom as between the axle-box and the guides. The axle-box, it is true, fits exactly between the faces of the guides without looseness, the distance apart of the guides being 10 inches; and it is constructed with flanges at each face, which overlap the guides, to keep the axle-box in position laterally with the frame; but these flanges are more widely apart by $1/_8$ inch than the width of the guides, for they are $6^7/_8$ inches apart, whilst the faces of the guides are $6^3/_4$ inches. A lateral play of $1/_8$ inch is thus permitted, and the total play, taken between the axle-journal and the guides, amounts to $(1/_8 + 1/_{16} =) \, 3/_{16}$ inch. The lateral play here signalised between the axle-box and the guides is not provided simply for the sake of easing the friction and the lubrication of the surfaces in contact; but also, and chiefly, for the purpose of securing freedom for the vertical movement of the axle-box, in cases where the wheel and its axle-box at one end of the axle may rise or fall whilst those at the other end may be stationary, in a vertical sense, or may be moved in the contrary direction. A radial movement of one end of the axle with respect to the other end is then induced; and the effect of it is that the flanges of the axle-box are set in inclination to the guides, and that thus they may be brought into contact with the guide at upper and lower corners diagonally. If there were no clearance, such as is here provided, the flanges would necessarily be broken off; but, with the clearance, they may assume a momentary inclination without incurring the risk of damage. The risk of accident from vertical oscillation of the axle in this manner is not so fanciful as one might imagine. The axle-box is 13 inches deep, and the total clearance between the flanges and the guides is $^1/_8$ inch. An inclination of $^1/_8$ inch in 13 inches, therefore, or one in 104, would suffice to bring up the surfaces into fixed contact; and, as the centres of the rails are, in this particular engine, 5 feet 8½ inches, or 68½ inches apart, it would only be necessary that they should be out of level with each other to the extent of $\dfrac{68.5}{104}$ = .66 inch, or about $^5/_8$ inch, to bring up the axle-boxes taut upon the guides. This is not a violent supposition, and it may be hoped that, when the inequality of level is more than $^5/_8$ inch, the frames may yield sufficiently to prevent ultimate fracture of the axle-box. In practice, they do so; for, without elasticity, less or more, everything would necessarily crumble to pieces.

The area of the bearing surface of one guide upon the axle-box is (6¾ inches wide by 13 inches deep =) 88 square inches. As the piston is 16 inches in diameter, or 201 square inches in area, it gives 2.30 square inches for each square inch of bearing on the axle-box. These proportions may be compared with those of the early Stephenson engine. The bearing surface of the outside axle-box on the guides in that engine amounted to 21½ square inches, and on the inside axle-box, next the wheel, to 11½ square inches: together 33 square inches for each 12-inch cylinder; the area of the piston was 113 square inches, or 3.42 square inches for each square inch of bearing on the axle-box. In the modern engine, a longer bearing surface is provided in proportion to the piston; but the working pressures of steam are also greater. It would, nevertheless, be making a more fitting comparison to regard only the inside bearing surface, next the crank, in the early engine; which, amounting only to 11½ square inches, offered only 1 square inch for every 10 square inches of the piston, or less than one-fourth in proportion of the surface provided in the modern engine.

The upper part, or crown, of the axle-box is formed as an arch over the axle, 1¾ inch thick at the summit, with a massive socket superadded to receive the end of the l¼-inch pin, through which the load on the spring is transmitted to the axle. The socket is stiffened by a transverse web across the crown within the four walls of the axle-box; a receptacle is formed for the tallow which is used as a lubricant, and is fed through two syphons, upon the journal of the axle, one syphon at each side of the axle-box; the syphons discharge the melted tallow into a groove cut in the under or bearing surface of the crown, which traverses the journal for the greater part of its length, and thus provides for the equal distribution of the lubricant. The sides of the axle-box are made nearly 1½ inch in thickness, that they may be capable of sustaining the alternate thrust of the steam-pressure through the crank upon the journal; and they are fortified by a bar of iron of flat section, which is cast in the body of the brass at each side and extends from the top to the bottom of the axle-box. The lower part of the axle-box is closed by a keep of cast-iron, which is fitted between the limbs of the axle-box, and laps close up to the journal; it is kept in its place by two wrought-iron pins which pass right through both the keep and the brass. The upper part of the axle-box is closed by lids of sheet-iron, hinged to the top of the box.

The leading and the trailing axle-boxes are constructed similarly to the driving-axle-box, with a closing front in addition, by which the ends of the axles are covered and protected. The guides provided for these are of cast-iron, riveted to the guards, which are forged on the outer longitudinal frame-plates.

Chapter 12

The Axles and Wheels

Crank-axle

The driving-axle, or crank-axle, is a fine piece of forged iron work, of massive proportions. The crank-axle is the least strong member in a locomotive engine, and it is only too obviously condemned by its form. To bring home the impression of the essential weakness of a crank-axle, one need only imagine such an axle, having two double-cranks, with four radial arms, erected on one end, and loaded upon the other end, treating it as a column. The lateral stress induced by blows given to it longitudinally through the wheels, when in rapid motion, corresponds to the load on the top of the column, with the aggravation that the end strains are the result of blows; and, what is more, the lateral blows are applied, not directly on end, but through the radial leverage of the wheel. The steam-pressure is another element of stress, though of less moment than the wheel-stress. Inside cranks are the despair of mechanical science, whether they be made of iron or of steel. The fatality is simply the effect of an overstraining of the crank beyond the limits of its elastic strength; and, from experience, the average life or duration of a crank-axle can be predicated within very narrow limits. Crank-axles usually fail by a cup-and-ball, or spherical-socket fracture at the 'pin,' which separates in this form from one of the crank-arms.

The crank-axle of the 'D. Luiz' is 7 inches in diameter between the cranks and at the journals; in the naves of the wheels, it is enlarged to a diameter of 8½ inches, where the length of bearing in the nave is 6¾ inches. The journals are 9 inches in length, and they extend between the naves of the wheels and the cranks. The crank-pins are 7¼ inches in diameter, slightly larger than the body of the axle; and they are 4½ inches in length, half the length of the journal. Their diametrical sectional-area is therefore (7¼ x 4½=) 32.6 square inches. Taking the maximum effective mean pressure on the piston at 100lbs per square inch, on the area 201 square inches, the total pressure that may be delivered upon the crank-pin would amount to (201 x 100=) 20,100lbs, or 9 tons, being at the rate of (20,100/32.6 =) 617lbs per square inch of diametrical section of the crank-pin. At high speeds, the maximum pressure may never exceed half of these calculated amounts. But even at low speeds, a pressure of 9 tons on each crank-pin would, when the cranks are in certain positions, result in a combined stress of 18 tons on the axle. The cranks, or crank-arms, are only 4f inches in thickness, but they are 10 inches broad, and each area presents a section of $(10 \times 4^3/_6 =)$ $43\frac{3}{4}$ square inches; whilst the section of the crank-pin is $41\frac{1}{4}$ square inches, and that of the journal is $38\frac{1}{2}$ square inches. Here it is apparent that the crank-arm is not quantitatively deficient in mass. The weakest part is, in reality, the crank-pin, which is over-stressed by forces operating through the leverage of the crank-arms; and it may be added that the most effective mode of strengthening a crank-axle is that which was long since adopted by Mr Gooch, now Sir Daniel Gooch – the enlargement of the diameter of the crank-pin relatively to the other parts of the axle.

It is scarcely necessary to add, that all the entering-angles of the axle are elaborately rounded, so that the essential weakness of square entering corners may be obviated.

Leading and Trailing Axles
The leading and trailing axles are, of course, straight. They are 6 inches in diameter at the middle portion between the wheels, and they are gradually increased to $6\frac{1}{2}$ inches in diameter at and within each wheel. There is a slight collar on the axle at each end, which acts as a shoulder or abutment, up to which the nave of the wheel is pressed, and which marks the precise position of the wheel on the axle when brought up to gauge. The bearings of the axles, which are outside the wheels, are 5 inches in diameter and 9 inches in length, presenting a diametrical section of $(5 \times 9=)$ 45 square inches for each journal, being 17 per cent, more than the diametrical section of the crank-axle, although the loads on the leading and trailing journals are less than those on the crank-axle journals. But, on the contrary, the leading axle and wheels have the onerous duty of guiding and steering the locomotive, plunging over and through all the inequalities of the line. The fatigue of the journals is, therefore, considerably more irregular than that on those of the driving-axle, and a liberal allowance of bearing surface is needful to ensure easy and cool working.

The journals on each axle, leading and trailing, are 7 feet apart between centres; those of the driving-axle are 4 feet $6\frac{1}{4}$ inches apart between centres.

Wheels
The leading and trailing wheels are, as before stated, 3 feet 9 inches in diameter, measured to the tread or rolling surface. The rims and the tyres are shown in section in Figs. 55, 56. They are solid wrought-iron wheels

forged in one piece, with the addition of tyres of Lowmoor iron. The nave, which is bored out to fit tightly on the axle, is 6 inches deep, and it is formed to a thickness of 3¼ inches round the axle. The rim is 5 inches wide and 1³/₈ inch thick at the middle of its width. The rim and the nave are united by 11 spokes, 1½ inch thick at the nave, and 1¹/₈ inch at the rim. The tyre is 5¼ inches wide, and 2¼ inches thick at the tread. It is shrunk hot on the wheel, and is fastened to it by rivets ⁷/₈ inch in diameter, with long conical heads through the tyre. By the conical form of the head, the rivet continues its hold on the tyre whilst the latter wears down in thickness. The taper of the cone is at the rate of 1 in 5, or, at each side, 1 in 10. The rivet-hole in the rim is partly countersunk at the inner face, and the rivet is formed with a conical head.

The nave of the driving-wheel is 6¾ inches wide, and is made with a thickness of 3¾ inches round the axle. The rim is 1¾ inch thick at the middle of its width, and is connected to the nave by 22 spokes. The tyre, of Lowmoor iron, is 2½ inches thick, and is fixed to the rim by conical rivets.

The number of spokes in each wheel is regulated by the frequency of, or intervals between, the spokes, necessary to afford a sufficient degree of

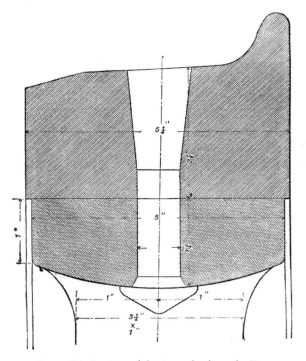

Figure 55. Section of driving-wheels at the Tyre.

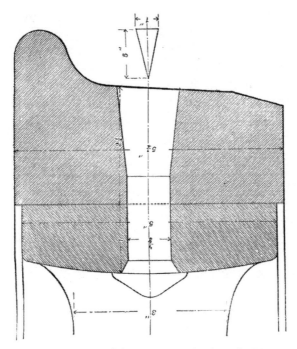

Figure 56. Section of the Carrying-wheels at the Tyre.

support to the rim. In the present instances, they are pitched at intervals of 10¾ inches, measured on the inner side of the rim, both for the larger and the smaller wheels; and, according to this gauge, the number of spokes increases a little faster than the diameter of the wheel. There are 11 spokes in the smaller wheels, and 22, or twice as many, in the larger wheels; but the diameter of the larger wheel is less than twice that of the smaller wheel.

The tyres of the leading and trailing wheels are formed to the normal section, Fig. 56, with flanges of full section; but the flanges of the driving-tyres, Fig. 55, are of reduced thickness. The object of this reduction of the flange is to ease the passage of the engine along curves, obviating more or less the jamming or tightening of the wheels by the binding of the flanges; and it has the advantage, moreover, of reducing the force of lateral blows upon the driving-wheels and the crank-axle. The full-size flange, Fig. 56, stands $1\frac{1}{8}$ inch above the centre of the tyre, and its medium thickness is $1\frac{1}{16}$ inch. The thinner flange, Fig. 55, is $\frac{11}{16}$ inch thick, or $\frac{3}{8}$ inch less than the other. These flanges are not so high as those of the early Stephenson engine, page 41, which stood $1\frac{7}{16}$ inch high. The difference is suggestive of the superior condition of the way in later, times, and the steadier movement of more recently designed engines; in virtue of which a less height of flange has been required for securing safety in running.

Each wheel is forced into its place on the axle by a hydraulic pressure of from 60 to 70 tons, and is secured on the axle with one steel key, for which a slot is cut partly in the axle and partly in the nave of the wheel. The key for the driving-wheel is $1^1/_2$ inch wide, and $^7/_8$ inch thick. Before this key would give way, it must fail by shearing; to effect the destruction of the key, which presents a shearing area of 10 square inches, a tangential force of at least 200 tons, applied at the circumference of the axle, at a radius of 4½ inches, would be required. This is equivalent to a force of

$$\frac{200 \times 4\frac{1}{2} \text{ inches}}{\frac{1}{2} \text{ stroke of piston}} = \frac{900}{11} = 82$$ tons at the crank-pin. It was found that

the maximum steam-stress at the crank-pin does not exceed 9 tons, and according to the ratio of 9 to 82, it would follow that the maximum steam-stress does not exceed one-ninth of the ultimate shearing-stress of the key. This calculation is put merely as one element of resistance; for, in addition to this, there is the resistance due to the grip-friction of the nave of the wheel upon the axle, as well as the modifying element of the momentum of the reciprocating parts.

Chapter 13

The Boiler

Shell

The barrel of the boiler and the fire-box-shell are constructed of iron plates ½ inch thick. The barrel is cylindrical, and is made of three rings of plates, with lap-joints, so that the middle ring is lapped upon the extreme rings. The interior diameter of the barrel, measured at the extreme rings, is 4 feet 2 inches; at the middle ring, it is more, by two thicknesses of plate, or 4 feet 3 inches. The length of the barrel, as made up, is 10 feet 8 inches between the fire-box-shell and the tube-plate at the smoke-box. The joints of the plates are single-riveted – united by a single row of rivets – with a lap of 2¼ inches, and ¾-inch, rivets placed at a pitch of 1¾ inch, as in Fig. 57. The fire-box-shell is turned at the upper part, which is semicircular, to a larger radius than the barrel – a radius of 2 feet 5 inches measured to the outside of the shell – making a width outside the shell of 4 feet 10 inches. The outside length of the shell is of the same dimensions, 4 feet 10 inches. The joints are lapped with single-riveting, as in the barrel; and the front and the back plates are flanged with a quadrantal bend to an inside radius of 2½ inches. The barrel is joined, by angle-irons at each end, to the fire-box-shell and the tube-plate, with single lines of rivets.

The great exterior dimensions of the boiler have been permitted by the wideness of the Spanish gauge, which is 9¼ inches more than the ordinary gauge. The greatest width of fire-box-shell that can be got in between the inside frame-plates of an engine of the 4-feet-8½-inch gauge, cannot be more than about 4 feet 1 inch. In the Spanish engine, the width of fire-box-shell is 9 inches more, and it has been adopted without causing inconvenience in the disposition of the other details. By reason of the enforced narrowness of the fire-box-

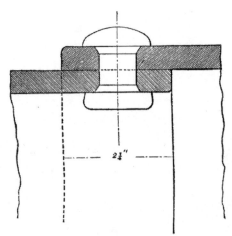

Figure 57. Single-riveted Lap

shells of the ordinary gauge, the upper portion of the shell only is enlarged, where it is tree from the restraint of the frame-plates, so as to form a crown of suitably large diameter for joining to the barrel of the boiler, and for providing steam-space, as will be exemplified farther on. But in the Spanish engine, on the contrary, the width of the shell is uniform from the upper part down to the bottom.

Fire-box

Equal latitude has been given to the internal fire-box, which occupies the entire length and width of the interior of the shell, minus a water-space 2½ inches wide, at the four walls, between the fire-box and the shell at the bottom, making the length and the width of the fire-box both 4 feet 3 inches inside. This space is slightly widened in ascending to the top of the fire-box, where it is 3 inches in width. The small inclination of the sides, here indicated, affords a slight degree of easement to the water and steam in the water-spaces; but it is questionable whether a greater width of water-spaces would not have been more efficient in facilitating the circulation there, and therefore increasing the rate at which the steam would have been generated and disengaged from the heating surfaces. In the early Stephenson locomotive, 3½ inches width of water-space was provided on all sides of the fire-box. This was comparatively good practice; and when it is considered that, from the fire-box, about 40 per cent of all the steam that is generated in the boiler is raised, there is strong reason for believing that water-spaces around the fire-box, of greater width than is usually given to them, would prove of greater efficiency.

The plates of the fire-box, of copper, are ½ inch thick. The tube-plate is thickened up to ¾ inch thick where the tubes are received.

The roof of the fire-box is flat and level, and it stands 5 feet 9 inches high, from the lower edge to the roof inside; or, from the level of the grate, 5 feet 5½ inches. It is united to the shell at the bottom by an iron ring or bar of rectangular section, sometimes called the foundation-ring, 2½ inches thick, with a single line of rivets. This bar is conveniently at hand for forming attachments for the grate and the ash-pan. The walls of the fire-box and the shell are also stayed together by screwed stay-bolts of copper, ⅞ inch in diameter, riveted over at each end. The stay-bolts are arranged in rows, and are pitched at a distance of 4 inches from centre to centre, both vertically and horizontally. At this pitch, the bolts are sufficiently near to each other to secure the benefit of the whole of the resistance of the bolts. When stay-bolts are very widely interspaced – at 9 inches apart, for instance – the plates are bulged between the stay-bolts to such an excessive degree, as to open up the screwed holes in the plates, and to disengage the threads of the internal screw from those of the external screw, ultimately loosening the hold of the bolt upon the plates, and leaving the whole of the bulging stress to be resisted by the rivet heads. It has been proved that, whatever means may be adopted for attaching the plates to the bolts, the surest element of ultimate resistance is supplied in pitching the bolts at comparatively short distances. It may be remarked that in the early Stephenson locomotive the stay-bolts were pitched at the same distance, 4 inches, as in the 'D. Luiz'.

The fire-doorway is cut through the back plates of the fire-box and the shell at a level, about 3 feet above the grate. It is slightly oval, being 12 inches high and 15 inches wide, and the junction of the plates is made with a east-iron ring of rectangular section, of a thickness sufficient to occupy the width of the water-space, and 2¼ inches in width, with a line of rivets.

Roof-stays of Fire-box

The roof of the fire-box is stayed by nine flat bars of iron, 5½- inches deep at the middle of their length, bolted to it with eleven bolts to each bar. Two of the bars are connected each by two links to the upper part of the fire-box-shell. These stay-bolts for the crown are pitched at 4.20 inches longitudinally and 4¾ inches transversely: – thus affording sufficient support for the roof, supposing that the bars themselves, having abutments over the front and the back plates of the fire-box, are sufficiently strong to sustain the pressure. The thickness of the bars is 1½ inch, and the distance apart of the points of support on the top of the fire-box is 50 inches. By the writer's formula,[15] the ultimate breaking-weight for one bar, applied at the middle, is:

$$W = \frac{26bd^2}{l} = \frac{26 \times 1\frac{1}{2} \times 5^2}{50} = 19\frac{1}{2}$$

or, uniformly distributed, (19½ x 2 =) 39 tons. Half of this, or 19½ tons, is the elastic limit of load, which should not be exceeded, regarding only the intrinsic strength of the bar itself. To find the actual maximum load in lbs pressure per square inch that maybe applied to each bar: – The pitch of the bars is 4¾ inches, and the span is 50 inches, giving an area of 237½ square inches of roof to be supported by one bar. The maximum pressure that may be applied, up to the elastic limit, is therefore (19½ x 2240/237½) 184lbs per square inch.

But, evidently, the bars are capable of sustaining more than this, since they are fortified by the crown-plate of the furnace, to which they are bolted at short intervals, and which aids them as a tie; and they might

15. 'A Manual of Rules, Tables, and Data,' 1877; page 589.

safely be submitted to the usual test-pressure of 200lbs per square inch, without being strained beyond the elastic limit. For a maximum steam-pressure of 150lbs, the load would amount to (237½ x 150/2240 =) 16 tons, which is well within the elastic limit of resistance of the bar itself, – reckoned above at 19½ tons.

This load leaves a margin of elastic resistance in the two bars which are linked to the roof, in virtue of which they may co-operate in distributing the aid that is derivable from the links over the roof of the fire-box. In a case of over-pressure on the roof, they would be capable, even in taking a set, of saving the fire-box from collapse on an emergency.

The total downward steam-pressure on the fire-box is measured by the horizontal area at the foundation-ring. The fire-box is just 6 inches shorter and narrower, mea¬sured to its outside, than the shell, or 52 inches square, giving a horizontal area of 2,704 square inches. At 150lbs per square inch, the total pressure on this area of surface would be (2,704 x 150/2,240 =) 181 tons. This load ie to be resisted by the rivets, in shear, in the foundation-ring; neglecting the auxiliary lateral resistance that may be offered by the stay-bolts and the doorway. There are about 120 ¾-inch rivets thus in shear, of which the ultimate shearing resistance is, at 16 tons per square inch of section, equal to 7 tons each; altogether (7 x 120 =) 840 tons, or about four and a half times the maximum steam-load. The elastic shearing resistance may thence be taken at about twice the steam-load. It may be said that the stay-bolts do not assist the foundation-ring in opposing vertical resistance ; for, certainly, when the steam is up and the fire is in an active condition, the vertical expansion of the fire-box is greater than that of the shell; and the stay-bolts, instead of opposing resistance to down¬ward action, may be strained upwards by the superior force of expansion of the fire-box, or, at the least, prevented from offering any resistance to downward pressure.

The weight of the boiler, including the barrel, fire-box-shell, and fire-box – not including the flue-tubes and the longitudinal stay-rods – amounts to 5 tons 9 cwts.

Tubes

The flue-tubes are of brass, 2 inches in diameter outside, and of tapering thickness: No. 12 Birmingham wire-gauge at the fire-box, and No. 14 at the smoke-box (or .103 inch and .083 inch respectively. Their average weight is 2.1lbs per lineal foot. They take their bearings in the tube-plates at each end of the barrel, between which, the span amounts to 10 feet 11 inches: – too long, certainly, for a tube without intermediate support. But the tubes are, in fact, supported by the water by which they are surrounded, and in which they are partially floated. The tubes are long

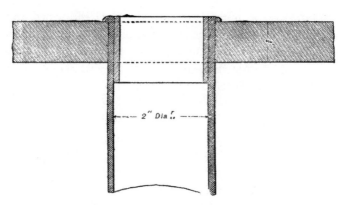

Figure 58. Fixing of Flue-tube into Fire-box Plate.

enough to pass through and project a little beyond the plates to which they are fastened upon; they are turned over, so as to form a small flange against the plate. In addition, they are blocked into the plates by steel ferules at each end, $1/8$ inch thick and $1\frac{1}{4}$ inch long, driven in tightly, flush with the outer end of the tube, as shown in Fig. 58. Fixed in this manner, the tubes not only are efficiently secured, but also act as stays for the plates. There are in all 215 tubes, disposed in fourteen horizontal rows, in which the tubes of one row alternate with the next, zigzag fashion. From the cross-section, Fig. 50, it appears that the water-section of the barrel is very fully occupied by tubes. It need only be remarked that there is too little clear space around the faggot of tubes to provide for the free circulation of the water, which, as is shown in Fig. 46, is delivered to the boiler at the middle of the barrel, and at the level of its centreline.

Again, for the reception of so large a number of tubes, it was necessary to place them at a distance apart of only $9/16$ inch. This amount of clearance is scarcely sufficient for the requirements of space for circulation, and there is no room for doubting that, if the tubes had been only $1^7/8$ inch in diameter, and spaced at the same intervals between their centres, so as to leave a clearance of $11/16$ inch between the tubes, the comparative efficiency of the boiler would have been superior to what it can be from the actual dimensions of the tubes. In continental locomotives, the accumulation of tubes has been ridiculously overdone, as if free circulation were not as much an item of necessity for evaporative performance, as heating surface.

Stays
The flat surface of the back-plate of the fire-box-shell, and the tube-plate at the fore end of the barrel, are stayed by two rows of $1\frac{1}{8}$ inch

stay-bolts, seen in the cross-section. The bolts are pitched at intervals of
4¾ inches, alternating, in fact, with the roof-stays of the fire-box. Each
bolt is formed with a head, and is screwed into the tube-plate of the
smoke-box, where it is introduced into the boiler. The other end of each
bolt is screwed, and is passed through the back-plate of the fire-box-shell,
to which it is fixed by a nut and a washer at each side of the plate. The
hole in the plate is plain. The screwed parts of the stay-bolts are 1³/₈ inch
in diameter. There is also a circular line of stay-bolts for the upper part
of the back-plate. They are made with palms, by which they are riveted
to the inside of the barrel. All the bolts are fixed with double nuts to the
back-plate and the front tube-plate. The long stay-bolts traversing the
barrel are supported at mid-length by cross-straps, to obviate the risk of
their sagging and working loose at the ends.

The fire-grate consists of a wrought-iron frame fitted within the fire-
box, at the bottom, on which two series of wrought-iron fire-bars are
supported. The fire-bars are 3½ inches in depth, ⁵/₈ inch thick at the top,
and ⁵/₁₆ inch at the lower edge, laid with air-spaces ½ inch wide. They are
thinned down towards the lower edge, to facilitate the inflow of air for
combustion. In the middle region of the fire-box a brick arch is constructed
from side to side, against the tube-plate, a little below the tubes. It is
inclined upwards, and reaches nearly half-way towards the doorway,
where the baffle-plate, of wrought-iron, is inserted, sustained by a flange
worked on it which takes a bearing on the outside of the doorway. The
baffle-plate reaches downwards and inwards exactly half-way towards
the tube-plate, and to a distance of 3 inches from the brick arch. It is
made of the same width as the doorway, 15 inches, and is formed to the
same curvature, so that the air which enters by the doorway is conducted
by the baffle-plate into the middle of the fire-box, dispersed right and left,
and intermixed with the combustible gases which rise from the coal on
the grate. The immediate contact and mixture of the gases and the air are
satisfactorily effected by the combined action of the arch, which deflects
the gases towards the back of the fire-box, and the baffle-plate, which
conducts the air to meet and to combine with the gases. But the arch
does more: being raised to a bright red heat, it maintains the combustible
gases which rise under it at a high temperature, and thus most materially
promotes and accelerates combustion.

The supply of air by the doorway is regulated by means of a pair of
sliding-doors, which are moved by hand, and slide horizontally in groove-
ledges, meeting at the middle when closed. They are connected by a pair
of levers in reverse, so linked together that the power applied by hand to
one lever suffices to move both doors simultaneously, as shown in Fig.
49. The combination of brick arch, baffle-plate, and sliding-door, it is

believed, was first introduced on the Midland Railway in or about the year 1860. The method of the brick arch, in combination with means of deflecting the supply of air introduced by the doorway, is now in general use in locomotives for burning coal. There appears, nevertheless, to be a considerable excess of air admitted for the purpose.

The ash-pan, applied at the bottom of the fire-box, and enclosing it, is constructed of ³/₈-inch plate. It is 13 inches deep, and is made with three fixed sides, and a swing damper in front, by the opening of which the supply of air through the grate may be regulated.

By means of the sliding fire-doors and the ash-pan damper together, the relative quantities of air supplied directly below or above the fire, may be adjusted in any desired proportions.

A fusible safety-plug is screwed into and through the crown-plate of the fire-box. It is made of brass, formed with a through core of lead ⁵/₈ inch in diameter. As the melting-point of lead is 617°F., whilst that of copper is about 2,000° F., the lead plug, if in good order, would melt before the copper could be injuriously overheated. At the same time, the melting-point of lead is far beyond the temperature of steam of 150lbs or even 200lbs.

The barrel and the upper part of the sides and the top of the fire-box-shell are clothed with a lagging of wood, covered with sheet-iron.

Heating-surface
The steam-generating function of the boiler is based mainly on the area of the fire-grate and the area of the heating-surface. The grate-area is 18 square feet, and the heating-surface is constituted as follows:

	Square
Surface of Fire-box	100.70
Surface of the Tubes, external	1238.40
	1339.10

The ratio of the grate-area to the heating-surface is 1 to 74.4.

Smoke-box
The smoke-box is 2 feet 6¼ inches long, measured inside between the tube-plate of the boiler and the front-plate. It is constructed of ³/₈ inch iron plates, riveted to the tube-plate, upon which a flange is turned to receive the plates, and connected at the front by angle-iron. The tube-plate and the front-plate are cut to fit the cylinder-castings, and these form the bottom of the smoke-box. The side-plates of the smoke-box are riveted to the upper edges of the inside frame-plates; and this constitutes the principal attachment of the boiler to the frame. A secondary attachment, which has already been mentioned, is made by means of the motion-plate, with two

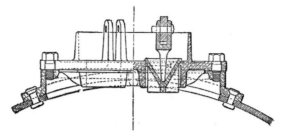

Figure 59. Manhole and Safety-valves.

riveted angle-irons. The boiler takes another bearing on the frame at the fire-box-shell, on each side of which a wrought-iron bracket is riveted, formed with a flat bearing which rests upon the upper edge of the frame-plate. There, the boiler, whilst it is firmly supported, is free for expansion and contraction longitudinally, for it is only fixed rigidly to the frame by the side-plates of the smoke-box. The motion-plate, it is true, supplies another point of fixture, but it is not very far from the smoke-box, and it is sufficiently flexible to yield to the slight extent of varying expansion and contraction which may take place between it and the smoke-box.

A circular hole, 17 inches in diameter, is cut in the crown of the smoke-box, over which the chimney is fixed. The chimney is made of sheet-iron, No. 9 gauge in thickness, riveted. It is 3 feet 7½ inches long, and consists of a bell-mouth base, by which it is riveted to the smoke-box; and a straight section, slightly taper, 14¼ inches in diameter inside at the lower end, and 13⅞ inches at the upper end.

Manhole

The manhole, Fig. 59, is cut through the fire-box-shell at the crown, and is 1 foot 5¾ inches in diameter. It is made up with a brass seating for the cover, flat on the upper side, ½ inch thick, and riveted to the shell. The upper side of the seating is made with a flange, to which the manhole-cover is bolted with ¾-inch stud-bolts and nuts. These bolts are pitched at 2⅝-inch centres, and they are 20 in number. The pressure which they have to resist is exerted upon a circle of 15 inches diameter – the diameter of the opening – having an area of, say, 177 square inches. The maximum pressure, at the rate of 150lbs per square inch, would amount to about 12 tons. The sectional area of a ¾-inch screw, at the base of the thread, is .307 square inch, making, for 20 screws, a total section of (.307 x 20 =) 6.14 square inches. At the rate of 12 tons per square inch, the total elastic strength of these bolts amounts to (12 x 6.14 =) 73.7 tons, or six times the maximum stress. The ultimate strength of the bolts is equal to twelve times the maximum stress.

Chapter 14

The Safety-Valves

The cover of the manhole is of brass, and it constitutes the seat for the safety-valves, of which there are two, side by side, as shown in Fig. 59. The seats are 2½ inches deep, and are bored to a diameter of 3½ inches. The valves are of the form of an inverted cone, hollow on the upper side, and they have three radial leaves or webs, which are turned to fit the interior of the seat, and serve as guides for the vertical movements of the valve. The rim of the valve is $3^5/_8$ inches in diameter, being $^1/_8$ inch larger than the interior of the seat. A border, having a projection of $^1/_{16}$ inch is thus left all round the valve, and it forms the seating for the valve, for which purpose the narrow surfaces of contact are bored and turned to the angle 45°. The pressure-pin of the lever takes its bearing on the bottom of the conical recess, which is at a level $1^7/_8$ inch below that of the surface of contact of the valve upon the seat. When, therefore, the valve is raised by the pressure of the steam, the centre of pressure of the steam being higher than the point of resistance at the pressure-pin, the effect is to maintain the valve truly central with the seating, in a condition of stable equilibrium, thus obviating any tilting action by which the valve could be jammed in the seating. In this regard, and also with respect to the width of the annular surface of the valve in contact with the seat, the modern valve is clearly superior to the safety-valve of the early Stephenson engine, page 20. The narrowness of the surface of contact renders the valve not only more nearly certain in its action, but also more susceptible to the action of excess-pressure.

Each valve is held to its seat by a wrought-iron lever, ¾ inch thick, pinned to a fulcrum, which is 4¼ inches from the centre bearing on the valve, and is 36½ inches long from the centre of the fulcrum to the centre of the spring-balance by which the lever is held down. The ratio of these distances $\left(\frac{36.5}{4.25}=\right)86$ is the expression of the leverage of the spring balance upon the valve. The area of each valve is 9.6 square inches.

Chapter 15

Steam-Pipes and Regulator

Steam is taken from the boiler for supplying the cylinders through a copper pipe, 5½ inches in diameter outside, and No. 10 Birmingham wire-gauge in thickness; which is placed within the barrel of the boiler, very near to the crown, and extends for the whole length of the barrel. It is closed at the ends, and is perforated at the upper part with numerous $1/8$-inch holes at ¼-inch pitch, through which the steam from the boiler is admitted and collected. A baffle-plate, or sheet, is fixed to the crown of the barrel at each side of the pipe, in order to separate and throw off any priming water that may rise with the steam. The pipe is let into a circular opening in the upper part of the tube-plate at the smoke-box, into which it is tightly wedged by a large iron ferule or ring, as shown in Fig. 60. Here it delivers the steam into the regulator-pipe, which is fixed in the upper part of the smoke-box. The body of the regulator, Figs. 60, 61, 62, is cylindrical in section, 4¾ inches in diameter inside; it is fitted with a segmental brass valve, which is adapted to the end of a rod placed concentrically within the regulator, by which it is turned radially within the body of the regulator. It rests on the lower part of the

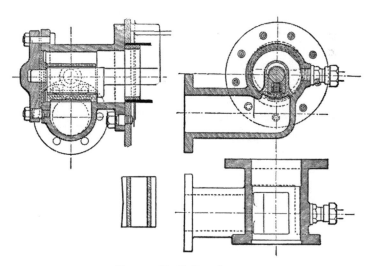

Figures 60–63. Regulator.

body, and covers a rectangular opening, which is 2½ inches in width, and 4 inches long, through which the steam must pass to the cylinder. The valve is, of course, made with lap at each side, and is 3¼ inches wide. But, in order that steam should be admitted very gradually to the cylinders, the lap on the steam-edge of the valve is indented, or formed as a V, to the extent of ⅛ inch. The effect of such want of straightness is, that, as the valve opens, steam is first of all admitted at the centre of the steam-edge, and it is only when the valve has travelled ⅛ inch, after the opening has commenced at the middle, that the steam-way is uncovered for its whole length of 4 inches. It is expedient that such means should be adopted for graduating the admission of the steam, at the commencement, into the pipe leading to the cylinders, for it aids in obviating the jar and distress to which the machinery is subjected when, at starting, steam is suddenly and fully turned on.

The valve, whilst it is free to adapt itself radially to its seat, by reason of a small extent of play which is allowed for the purpose, is, nevertheless, held to its seat by a small vertical spring, which imposes a constant degree of pressure upon it in addition to the pressure of the steam in the boiler.

The valve receives its radial movement by means of a long rod carried through the steam-pipe and the fire-box-shell to the back of the shell, where it passes through a stuffing-box, and is fitted with a double-handled lever, each arm of which is 18 inches in length, in front of the engine-driver. To estimate the resistance of the regulator-valve, the area of the valve subject to the pressure of the steam may be taken as (3¼ x 4¾ =) 15.44 square inches, on which the maximum load, at 150lbs per square inch of steam pressure, amounts to 2,316lbs. Taking the friction as 10 per cent, of the pressure, it amounts in this instance to (2316 x 10/100=) 232lbs. The leverage of the regulator-handle is as 18 inches radius to 2⅜ inches, the radius of the valve, or as 1 to 7½; and the pressure at the handle required to overcome the friction of the valve would be (237/7½ =) 31½lbs. If the pressure in the boiler be taken at 120lbs per square inch, the resistance at the handle would be only four-fifths of the above, or 25lbs.

The steam, after having passed the regulator, flows into a short cast-iron pipe, 3½ inches in diameter and ⁹⁄₁₆ inch thick, in the smoke-box; from which the steam is conducted through a copper pipe, 3¾ inches in diameter, led round the inside of the smoke-box to the valve-chest between the cylinders.

Chapter 16

The Glass-Gauge and the Whistle

The glass-gauge, for showing the level of the water in the boiler, is fixed to the back of the fire-box-shell, at the right-hand side. The glass tube is ⁵/₈ inch in diameter outside, and No. 12 Birmingham wire-gauge in thickness. It is held between two brass standards screwed to the boiler, and is introduced through an opening in the top of the upper standard, which is closed by a screw-plug. It is made steam-tight in the standards by a stuffing-box to each standard. Each standard is fitted with a cock, by which it may be closed when required; and the lower standard has an additional cock below the tube, through which, when opened, the steam and water may be blown off to clear the passages. The waste water is led away below the foot-plate by a ³/₈-inch copper tube. Each standard is fitted with a screw-plug opposite the passage from the boiler, so that, by unscrewing the plugs, the passages may be cleared of solid matter that may accumulate. A lamp-holder is fixed close by, to show the water-level by lamp at night. The normal water-level in the boiler stands 2½ inches high in the glass, and is 6 inches above the crown of the fire-box when the engine stands on a level.

Two gauge-cocks are fixed to the back of the fire-box-shell, at the left-hand side, for testing the water-level when the gauge-glass is not in good order.

The pressure-gauge, having a circular dial, is supported by and attached to the weather-board on the crown of the fire-box. Communication with the boiler is made through a ⁵/₁₆-inch copper tube, connected to a brass cock screwed into the crown of the shell. The tube makes 1½ turns in a circle 3½ inches in diameter, to provide the needful elasticity between the gauge and the cock.

The whistle is of brass, with a bell 3³/₁₆ inches in diameter outside. Steam is issued as an annular jet, of a diameter nearly equal to that of the bell, ¹/₃₂ inch in thickness. The steam is admitted to the whistle through a small disc-valve, ¾ inch in diameter, opened by a quick-thread screw-motion.

Chapter 17

Boiler Now Constructed

The system of construction now adopted for locomotive boilers by Messrs. Beyer, Peacock, and Co, is illustrated by Fig. 63, and showing a boiler adapted for the 4 feet 8½ inch gauge. It comprises the telescopic construction, the double riveting of the longitudinal seams, and the fortifying of the man-holes. In the telescopic construction, the barrel is constructed in rings of diminishing diameter, the first of which is

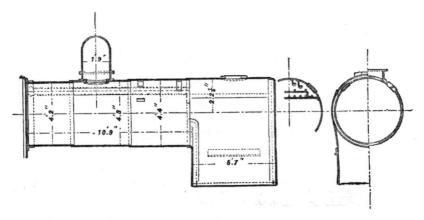

Figure 63. Boiler now constructed by Messrs. Beyer, Peacock, and Co

lapped inside the fire-box-shell, the second inside the first, and the third inside the second. The junction of the fire-box with the barrel is thus reduced to a simple lap-joint, by the aid of the flanging of the front plate below, and the boiler has the appearance of a flush top. As all the circular plates are ½ inch in thickness, the effect of the telescopic arrangement is to diminish the diameter by 1 inch at a time, and the successive diameters are as follows:

	Diameter Outside		Diameter Inside	
	Ft	In	Ft	In
Fire-box-shell	4	5	4	4
1st Ring of Barrel	4	4	4	3
2nd Ring of Barrel	4	3	4	2
3rd Ring of Barrel	4	2	4	1

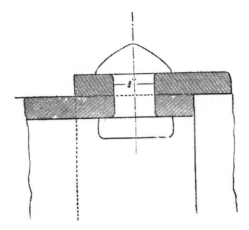

Figure 64. Single-riveted Lap-joint of the Boiler.

Such an arrangement is in keeping with the relative evaporative action of the several portions of the boiler; making also an economy of material, of weight, and of workmanship.

With respect to the joints of the plates, whilst the circular and vertical seams of the boiler are single-riveted, as shown in Fig. 64, the longitudinal seams of the fire-box-shell are double-riveted, and those of the barrel are butt-joints, with double welts or strips, of which one is applied inside the joint and the other outside, double-riveted to each plate. It is seen, in the figures, that the longitudinal seams break joint, and that they are disposed in the upper portion or steam-space of the boiler. They are to this extent out of the reach of corrosive action by the water, and the grooving to which ordinary lap-joints are subject is obviated by the method of construction, in which the stress and the strain caused by the internal pressure of the steam are transmitted centrally through the body of the plate. The writer, in 1859, traced the cause of grooving to its source, and he then recommended the adoption of double-riveted double welt-joints for the longitudinal seams of locomotive boilers, and single-riveted lap-joints for the circular seams: – a recommendation which has been followed in the best recent practice of locomotive engineers.[16]

Thirdly, the fortifying of the man-holes is effected by riveting to the plate, round each man-hole, wrought-iron rings. The openings are restricted to the smallest diameter practicable, so that in all respects the reduction of strength may be minimised. The man-hole in the crown of

16. For an extended discussion of the strength of riveted joints, see 'Railway Locomotives', 1860, pages 2* to 12*; also 'A Manual of Rules, Tables, and Data', 1877, page 634, &c.

the fire-box-shell, which was cut to a diameter of about 18 inches in the 'D. Luiz', is, in the latest boiler, Fig. 63, only 13 inches in diameter, whilst the opening to the steam-dome on the barrel is only 16 inches in diameter, whilst the dome itself is 21 inches. This opening, moreover, is strengthened by two rings riveted to it, one above and one below the plate. These modifications are judicious; their necessity, for the purpose of maintaining the ultimate strength of the boiler, has been clearly demonstrated by the results of the experimental investigations of Mr Lavington E. Fletcher on the

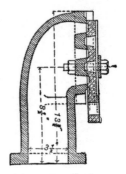

Figure 65. Regulator.

strength of Lancashire boilers. The rivet-holes of the most recent boiler are not countersunk, but are simply cylindrical, having the arris removed at each end. The form of regulator adopted for this boiler is shown in Fig. 65. A plate-valve, formed with ports, slides upon a vertical face, formed similarly with ports, for the admission of steam to the steam-pipe.

Chapter 18

The Cylinders and Valves

The steam-cylinders, one of which is shown in Fig. 66, are 16 inches in diameter, and are made for a stroke of 22 inches. They are of cast-iron, of very hard quality, and are 1 inch thick in the body. They are bored out at the ends to a larger diameter, 16¼ inches, to receive the covers, one at each end, which are turned to fit into them accurately. The covers are peculiarly formed, with undulating surfaces, to correspond with the shape of the piston, so as to provide a clearance-space between the piston when at each end of the stroke, and the cover, of ³/₈ inch. The front cover of each cylinder is hollowed on the outer surface to correspond with the form of the internal surface, so as to provide a thickness of ⁷/₈ inch, with flanges 1¹/₈ inch thick. The hollow is enclosed with a sheet-iron disc.

The back cover is more strongly made than the front cover, as it carries the ends of the guide-bars. It has a flat face inside, and is made 1⁵/₁₆ inch thick; an annular lump of cast-iron is riveted to the inner surface, to occupy the waste space which is caused by the form of the piston, excepting the ³/₈ inch clearance-space already mentioned. The back cover is formed with a stuffing-box for the piston-rod, 4 inches in diameter inside, sufficient for the reception of packing, ¾ inch thick round the piston-rod. A brass collar is let into the bottom of the stuffing-box, and the box is closed with a brass gland of oval form, tightened upon the packing by means of two ¾-inch bolts with double nuts. The gland is made up square at one side, and hollowed to form an oil-cup, from which the oil for lubrication is delivered by a syphon to the piston-rod. The cup is closed by a hinged lid. Two wings are cast on the back cover, one on each side of the stuffing-box, to receive the two pairs of guide-bars. They are 2¾ inches in thickness, being sufficiently thick to make up, with two packing pieces of ¹/₈-inch sheet copper, the required width apart of the guide-bars, 3 inches.

The cylinder-covers are fastened to the cylinders, each with ten ⁷/₈-inch stud-bolts and nuts. The bolts are screwed into the flanges at the ends of the cylinder, 1 inch thick, and are formed each with a salient angle at one side, where they pass through the cover, to afford a purchase for screwing them into the flanges of the cylinders, and that they may be prevented

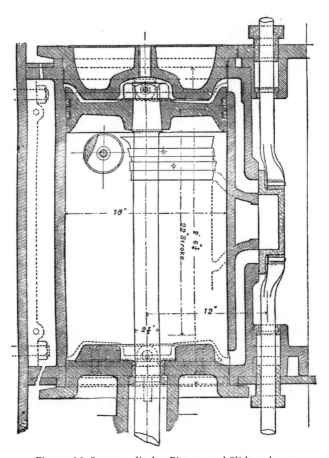

Figure 66. Steam-cylinder, Piston, and Slide-valve.

from turning round and working loose. They are pitched at distances of 6 inches for the most part; and it may be well to calculate the margin of strength which they possess as against the pressure in the cylinder. Taking the maximum pressure as before at 150lbs per square inch, the surface of the cover presents to the steam an area 16¼ inches in diameter, amounting to 207.4 square inches, and the total pressure resisted amounts to (150 x 207.4/2240 =) about 14 tons. Now, each ⁷/₈-inch screwed bolt is .733 inch in diameter at the bottom of the thread, for which the sectional area is .537 square inch; and, for 10 bolts, the united section amounts to (.537 x 10 =) 5.37 square inches. The gross pressure for each bolt is (14/10 =) 1.4 tons, and per square inch of section it is (14/5.37 =) 2.61 tons – about one-tenth of the ultimate strength of the best bolt-iron.

The steam-chest between the two cylinders is of liberal width. As the centres of the cylinders are 32 inches apart, the space between the cylinders is equal to (32 − (16 x 2) =) 14 inches. Each valve-face stands 2½ inches from the cylinder, and the distance apart of the valve-faces is (14 − (2¼ x 2) =) 9½ inches, which is available for placing the slide-valves with 4½ inches of clear width of space between the backs of the valves, and leaving plenty of room for the movements of the steam. Here, there is no cause of such embarrassment as is met with in the arrangement of the corresponding parts of the locomotives constructed for the 4 feet 8½ inch gauge. At the near end of the valve-chest the 3¾-inch steam-pipe delivers the steam from the boiler. The front end of the valve-chest is closed by a cast-iron cover, 1⅛ inch thick, with which are cast the stuffing-boxes for the valve-spindles. It is fixed with 16 bolts ⅞ inch in diameter.

Two drain-taps are screwed into the lower side of each cylinder, one at each end and one into the valve-chest, for letting off water that accumulates there.

The steam-ports to the ends of the cylinder are 1⅜ inch wide and 13 inches long, and the width of the exhaust-port is 3½ inches. The bars between the ports are 1 inch wide. The slide-valve is made without any inside lap or clearance – 'line-and-line'; the outside lap at each end of the valve is 1 inch, making the total length of the valve 10¼ inches. The cavity of the valve is 2⅛ inches deep – a medium between the widths of the steam-port and the exhaust-port. The valve works upon the face of the cylinder between two lateral guiding surfaces, which are planed out to receive the valve. The valve naturally rests and slides on the lower ledge, which thus relieves the spindle of the weight of the valve.

The maximum travel of the slide-valve is 4 inches. It is less than the throw of the excentrics, inasmuch as the excentric-rods are connected to the extremities of the link, where, of course, the slide-block cannot be brought into line with either excentric-rod. The excentrics are so set or the axle as to give a lead of ¼ inch to the valve.

The valve-spindle is 1½ inch in diameter, and takes its bearing through stuffing-boxes in the front and the back of the valve-chest. It is worked as a frame or bridle, to embrace the rectangular back of the slide-valve. The stress on the spindle caused by the effort required to move the valve is calculated approximately from the pressure of the steam and the area of the valve. The area of the back of the valve is equal to (10¼ x 15½ =) 159 square inches; and, taking the maximum pressure of steam in the valve-cheat at 120lbs per square inch, the total pressure on the back of the valve is (159 x 120 =) 19,080lbs. Allowing 10 per cent, of the pressure as the value of the frictional resistance, this would amount to 1,908lbs, or nearly 1 ton. The sectional area of the spindle is 1¾ square inch, and obviously the estimated stress lies far within its absolute tensile strength. It is, nevertheless, to be noted that the valve-spindle is not straight, and that there is necessarily much transverse stress on the frame over the valve. It is, moreover, to be noted that the frictional resistance of the valve, after having been at rest for some time, may often very much exceed the normal resistance whilst at work.

Each of the cylinders is cast as one piece with one half of the valve-chest. The valve-chest is $7/8$ inch thick. The two castings are bolted together by flanges, 1 inch thick, with ¾-inch bolts and nuts. On the outer side of each cylinder, the ribs, $15/16$ inch thick, are cast, by which the cylinder is united, with flanges $1^1/8$ inch thick, to the inside frame-plate, with 1-inch bolts and nuts. The length of the cylinder-castings over the front and back flanges – which fit between the tube-plate and the front-plate of the smoke-box – is 2 feet 6¼ inches, which, as before stated, is the length of their bearing on the frame-plate at each side.

The guide-bars are of steel, and are arranged in two pairs to each cylinder. The bara are 3 inches wide, and are 3 inches apart in each pair, to receive the guide-blocks between them. The two pairs are placed 6¾ inches apart, on each side of the stuffing-box of the cylinder, and each pair is bolted to the wings on the cover with two ¾-inch bolts and nuts. The nuts are secured by split-pins passed through the bolts. The guide-bars are 1¼ inch thick at the ends, and swelled gradually to a thickness of 2 inches at the middle of their length. The outer end of each bar is secured by one bolt and nut to a distinct block, which is bolted to the motion-plate.

Chapter 19

The Blast-Pipe

The exhaust-steam is discharged almost directly into the blast-pipe, which is of cast-iron, ½ inch thick, and rises direct from the cylinders. It is fitted with a plate on the top, bolted to it, having an orifice of the precise diameter required – 4½ inches – for inducing the proper action of the blast. This plate is at a level 21 inches below the crown of the smoke-box: in fact, it is level with the uppermost row of tubes. The level best adapted for inducing the draught of the boiler was not known in the designing of the early Stephenson engine, in which the blast-pipe was carried up into the interior of the chimney. The short blast-pipe of the 'D. Luiz' yields the best results, creating a better draught with a wide orifice as compared with higher blast-pipes. It was arrived at by Mr Peacock by means of a series of well-arranged experiments, made by him, in 1850, on the Manchester, Sheffield, and Lincolnshire Railway. The low blast-pipe is now generally employed. The high blast-pipes had very contracted orifices and a sharp blast, causing much back-pressure on the piston. It has already been shown, page 115, that with proper proportions there is not, in practical working, any back-pressure of exhaust – a result to the realisation of which Mr Peacock's experimental investigation contributed in a material degree.[17]

A ring-jet is placed upon the top of the blast-pipe, supplied with steam through a small tube from the regulator. The tube is led through the smoke-box, where a small cock is adapted to it on the outside, and is worked by a rod from the foot-plate. By a return-tube, the steam is conducted to the ring-jet. This is a portion of the same tube turned into a ring, and perforated with a number of small holes on its upper side. Through these holes, when the steam is turned on, a number of jets of steam are projected into the chimney, by which a mild draught may be sustained when the steam is shut off from the engine. It is useful for keeping up the fire, and, to some extent, preventing the escape of visible smoke by the chimney.

---

17. For a detailed account of Mr Peacock's experiments, see 'Railway Machinery', page 134.

Chapter 20

Pistons and Crossheads

The pistons, Fig. 66, are of cast-iron, each in one piece, consisting of a nave and a rim united by a web. The rim is 4¼ inches broad, and has two grooves turned in it, ½ inch apart, to receive the packing-rings. The grooves are each ¾ inch wide and ⁷/₁₆ inch deep. The springs, of brass, are also ¾ inch wide, making a good and easy fit in the grooves, and are ³/₈ inch thick. They are thus, when in place, left with a clearance of ¹/₁₆ inch between them and the bottoms of the grooves. Each ring is turned in one piece to a diameter ¹/₈ inch larger than that of the cylinder. A short piece is cut out, and the ends of the spring brought together in the groove, where it is prevented from shifting by a stud-pin. The nave is 4⁵/₈ inches in diameter, and is 3 inches deep. It is bored conically to fit the end of the piston-rod, which is tapered from a diameter of 3 inches to one of 2⁵/₈ inches – making a taper of 1 in 8. A nut, 1½ inch thick, is screwed on to the end of the piston-rod. beyond the taper portion, and thus the piston is secured.

Here is a remarkably simple piston, contrasting strongly with the heavy and complex piston of earlier times (page 25). The piston-rod, it has already been said, is 2½ inches in diameter; the outer end is reduced to 1³/₈ inch in diameter, and is formed with a slight taper – 1 in 32 on the diameter – for a length of 5 inches, which is received in a socket formed on the crosshead. The rod is secured with a cotter, ⁵/₈ inch thick and 1⁷/₈ inch wide at the middle. The cotter, being in double-shear, has a shearing section of, say (1⁷/₈ x ⁵/₈ x 2 =) 2.34 square inches, for resisting a maximum pressure of 150lbs per square inch on the piston, having 201 square inches of area, amounting to (201 x 150/2240 =) 13½ tons. This is at the rate of (13.5/2.34 =) 5.77 tons per square inch. The ultimate shearing strength of cotter-steel is – say 22 tons per square inch – nearly four times the maximum stress that may be thrown upon the cotter. The stress on the piston-rod, having a sectional area of 4.9 square inches, is at the rate of (13.5/4.9 =) 2¾ tons per square inch. The cotter in the crosshead is prevented from working out, by a split-cotter passed through the narrower end of it, and the split-cotter is itself secured by a smaller split-pin.

The crosshead-pin is 2¾ inches in diameter, reduced at each end to 1¾ inch, within the slide-blocks. Each pin is extended beyond the slide, at one side, to receive the head of the pump-ram, which is worked by it. The width of the bearing for the connecting-rod on the cross-pin is 2¾ inches. A diametrical section of bearing, having an area of (2¾ x 2¾ =) 7.56 square inches, is thus presented, for communicating the working stress to the connecting-rod. Taking the maximum average working stress on each piston at 9 tons, as was before estimated (page 129), it is equivalent to a pressure of (9/7.56 =) 1.19 tons, or 2,667lbs per square inch of diametrical section.

Chapter 21

Connecting-Rod

The connecting-rod is 6 feet in length from centre to centre, having six and a half times the length of the crank. The brasses at the small and the large end are respectively bored and turned to the same dimensions as the cross-head-pin and the crank-pin. The body of the rod – the plain part between the two ends – is flat-sided, being $1\frac{7}{8}$ inch thick, and it is turned at the upper and lower surfaces. The middle part is tapered uniformly in depth between the ends, being 3 inches deep at the small end and 4 inches at the large end.

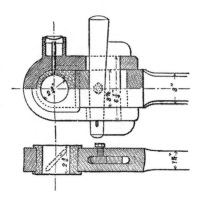

Figures 67–68. Connecting-rod. Small End.

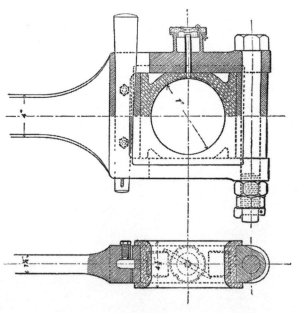

Figures 69–70. Connecting-rod. Large End.

Each end is necessarily enlarged, so as to make a bearing and a fixture for the brasses. The smaller end, Figs. 6 7, 68, is thickened to 2¼ inches wide and 3⅝ inches deep; between this abutment and a bent strap the brasses are held, and are tightened by a gib and a cotter passed through the butt and the strap. These are ¾-inch thick, and the cotter is fixed by a small split-cotter through the lower end, and by a ⅝-inch set-screw. The large end, Figs. 69, 70, is thickened to 3⅝ inches wide, and is formed as a fork, with upper and lower branches, to embrace and overhang the brasses; the branches being bound together behind the brasses by a 1⅞-inch bolt with two nuts at the lower end, secured by a split-cotter passed through the bolt, the cotter itself being secured by a split-pin. The ends of the two forks are strutted apart by a block of wrought-iron, through which the bolt is passed, and which is formed with a flat face to give a fixed bearing to the brass in front of it. The brasses are square outside, and are brought together by a cotter at the other side, 1 inch thick, secured by a split-pin and by two ⅝-inch set-screws. The pressure of the cotter is taken directly by a plate of steel, which bears upon the back of the brass next to it. The upper and lower branches of the fork are 8¼ inches apart, to make room for the crank-pin, 7¼ inches in diameter, and ½ inch of brass above and below it. The brasses are each 1¼ inch thick fore and aft of the crank-pin. An oil-cup is forged solid on each end of the connecting-rod, and is closed with a brass cover. The oil is syphoned through a ⅜-inch copper tube to the bearing, over which it is distributed by a groove cut diagonally m the crown of the brasses.

Chapter 22

Valve-Gear

The valve-gear is designed with the straight-link motion. For each cylinder there are two excentrics – the fore and the back – with their rods, the straight expansion-link, and the radius-rod, pinned to the valve-spindle. The excentrics, Figs. 71, 72, are of cast-iron, 15 inches in diameter and 2½ inches wide; and a recess is turned out at each side at the circumference, to afford a hold for the brass hoop which surrounds each excentric. The excentric is made in two halves, united upon the driving-axle by two 1-inch bolts, secured into the smaller half, and cottered to the larger. As the radius of the excentric is 2¾ inches, a minimum thickness of 1¼ inch is left round the axle. The excentric is fastened by a ½-inch square steel key, let, by half its thickness, into the axle; and also by a ¾-inch steel set-screw. The excentric-strap, or hoop, is

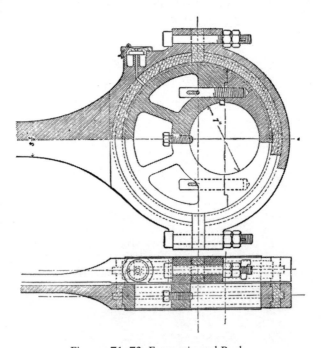

Figures 71–72. Excentric and Rod.

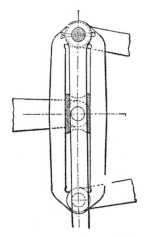

Figure 73. Expansion-link.

of wrought-iron, $2^3/_8$ inches wide and $1^1/_8$ inch thick, in two halves, bolted together by flanges, and a $^7/_8$-inch bolt with two nuts and a split-cotter at each side. The hoop has a brass lining, $^5/_8$ inch thick; and there are two brass packing pieces, $1\frac{1}{4}$ inch thick, inserted for taking up wear at the junctions of the half-hoops. The nearer half-hoop of each excentric is forged solid with the excentric-rod, which is of such a length that the distance from the centre of the hoop to the centre of the joint-pin at the other end of the rod is 3 feet $9\frac{1}{2}$ inches. A syphoning oil-cup is forged solid on the excentric-strap, and has a brass cover screwed on it, secured by a split-pin. The excentric-rod is flat in section, $\frac{3}{4}$ inch thick, $3\frac{1}{2}$ inches deep near the hoop, and 2 inches deep near the other end.

The expansion-link, Fig. 73, is $2\frac{1}{2}$ inches thick, and is 16 inches long between the centres at the ends, to which the excentric-rods are connected by $1\frac{1}{2}$-inch pins. The radius-rod is of the same length as the excentric-rods – 3 feet $9\frac{1}{2}$ inches – and it carries on a $1\frac{1}{2}$-inch pin at its extremity the expansion slide-block, which is of steel, $3\frac{3}{4}$ inches long, and works in the expansion-link, the opening of which is parallel-sided, $2\frac{1}{2}$ inches wide. The expansion-link and the radius-link are sustained by links from the ends of levers of unequal lengths, on the reversing shaft. This shaft is $3\frac{1}{4}$ inches in diameter, and works in bearings fixed to the inside frame-plates; the levers are, respectively, $2^7/_8$ inches long for supporting the expansion-link, and 6 inches long for supporting the radius-link. The first supporting link is attached to the expansion-link at the upper centre; the second is attached to the radius-link at a distance of $7\frac{1}{4}$ inches from the centre of the expansion-block. These special measurements, taken together, are the result of tentative efforts to establish an equal distribution of steam to the cylinder, together with easy movements in the gearing.

Chapter 23

Feed-Pumps and Injector

The boiler is fed or supplied with water by means of two pumps, one of which is worked from the crosshead of each piston-rod, as shown in the plan, page 117. The body of each pump is of brass, $^7/_{16}$ inch thick, and is bored out to a diameter of $1^7/_8$ inch, which is the diameter of the ram. It is bolted to the inside frame-plate. The ram is cottered to a socket which is pinned to the outer end of the crosshead-pin, and the stroke of the ram is, of course, equal to that of the piston. The waterways to and from the pump are $1\frac{3}{4}$ inch in diameter, and the water is brought from the tender through a copper pipe of the same diameter. There are three ball-valves, or clacks, for each pump; of which the first and second, Figs. 74, 75, are immediately below and immediately above the body of the pump; and the third is placed close to the boiler, the water reaching to it through a $1\frac{3}{4}$-inch copper pipe from the second valve. The valves or balls are 2 inches in diameter, and they are confined by cages, in which they are only permitted to rise from their seats through a very limited height. The lift of the first ball is restricted to $^3/_{16}$ inch; that of the second ball is permitted to be $^1/_8$ inch; and that of the third ball, at the boiler, to be $\frac{1}{4}$ inch. The successive augmentation of the range of the balls in lifting is designed for the purpose of facilitating the passage

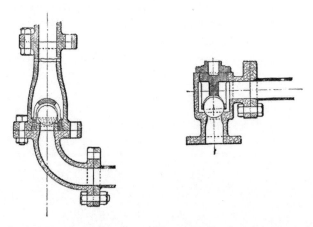

Figure 74. Feed-pump. Lower Ball-valve.   Figure 75. Feed-pump. Upper Ball-valve.

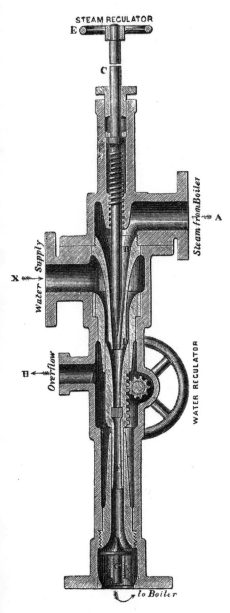

Figure 76. Injector.

of the water; for, once it is taken in and has passed the first valve, it must needs pass through the other valves or burst the pump. The additional lift, then, given to the second and the third valves, is a security that whatever water may be passed through the first valve will, with certainly at least as much facility, be passed through the other two. The seats of the valves are of less diameter than the pipes. The first and second are $1^7/_{16}$ inch in diameter, and the third is a little larger, 1½ inch. The surface of contact of each valve on its seat is very narrow, – about $1/_{16}$ inch wide. By such limitation r of width, sensitiveness and promptitude of action are much augmented in the new pump as compared with the old pump (page 34). Indeed, the contrast between these pumps is remarkable, and it affords evidence of what may be gradually accomplished by intelligent experience.

Since the stroke of the pump is equal to that of the piston, the maximum volume of water that may be passed by one pump, is to the volume of the cylinder as the sectional area of the ram is to that of the piston, or it is as $(1^7/_{16})^2$ to 16^2, or as 3½ to 256, or 1 to 73. According to this ratio, one pump would supply water for a volume of steam equal to four times the relative capacity of one cylinder, or (73 x 4 =) 292 times the volume of the pump, which is single-acting. Now, 292 is the relative volume of steam of 92lbs absolute pressure, or 77lbs effective pressure per square inch; and steam having this terminal pressure, if cut-off at, and expanded from, 75 per cent, of the stroke would have the initial absolute pressure (92 x 102/75 =) 123lbs, or 108lbs effective initial pressure. As so high a pressure as this is not associated with an admission of so much as 75 per cent, it may be assumed that, in general, one pump in full action is at least sufficiently powerful to keep up the supply of feed-water for the boiler.

An injector is placed at the side of the fire-box-shell as an alternative for the pumps. The water is delivered by it direct to the boiler, through the fire-box-shell, at the entrance to which a delivery ball-valve is placed. The lift of the valve is ½ inch, which is twice as much as is allowed for the third valve connected with the pumps.

A common form of injector is illustrated by Fig. 76. Steam from the boiler is admitted at A, into the injector at B, and passes through the nozzle D and the passage F, and past the valve G into the boiler. By the suctional action of the current of steam, water is drawn in through the pipe x, and is carried with the steam, which is partly condensed, into the boiler. The supplies of steam and of water are regulated by hand-wheels.

Chapter 24

The Tender

The tender of the 'D. Luiz' locomotive is carried on three pairs of wheels, 3 feet 9 inches in diameter, placed at intervals of 6 feet between centres, and making a wheel-base of 12 feet. The tank is 16 feet 6 inches in length, and 6 feet 3 inches wide, outside measure. It is 3 feet $^5/_8$ inch deep inside, and it has a capacity for 1,780 gallons, or 8 tons, of water. The sides and the end are carried up to a height of 9 inches above the roof of the tank, forming storage for coal, of which altogether 140 cubic feet may be placed on the tender. Allowing $44^1/_2$ cubic feet of heaped coal per ton, there is room on the tender for (140/44½ =) over 3 tons of coal. The total height of the tender is 7 feet 10 inches above the level of the rails; and the width, over the platform, is 8 feet. The wheels, axles, axle-boxes and bearing-springs are constructed like the leading and trailing wheels and appurtenances of the locomotive. The journals are 4 inches in diameter and 8 inches long; and the axles are 5½ inches in diameter within the naves of the wheels, and 5 inches at the middle.

The frame of the tender consists of four longitudinal frame-plates, two at each side; of which the outer plates are formed with axle-guards to take the axle-boxes. The two outer plates are 7 feet 2 inches apart; and the two inner plates are 5 feet apart. The frame is made up with

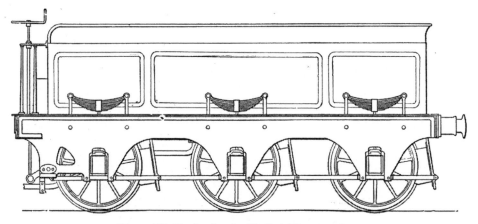

Figure 77. Tender for the 'D. Luiz' Locomotive.

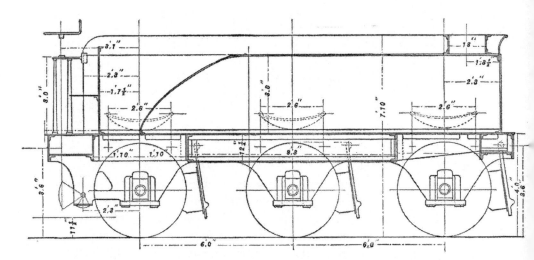

Figure 78. Tender. Longitudinal Section.

five transverse plates, and angle-iron fastenings; and with the platform covering the whole frame, and securely united to it, a strong frame is produced. The brake is applied to all the wheels of the tender, one block behind each wheel, and is worked by means of a vertical screw, having a double lever at the upper end, acting on levers under the foot-plate, with connections to the blocks.

Section IV: Resistance of Trains

Chapter 25

Experimental Resistance

The resistances of engines and trains are of two kinds: – the frictional resistance to traction on a line of rails, and the resistance of gravitation on inclined planes on railways, when they are ascended by the train. With respect to the resistance to traction, the writer constructed a simple formula, embracing the results of Sir Daniel Gooch's experiments,[18] for the resistance on a level line of rails, of the engine, tender, and train:

$$R = 8 + \frac{v^2}{171}$$

v = the speed in miles per hour.
R = the total resistance of the engine, tender, and train, per ton gross, measured at the rails.

Rule
To find the total resistance of the engine, tender, and train at a given speed. – Square the speed in miles per hour, divide it by 171, and add 8 to the quotient. The sum is the total resistance reduced to the rails, in lbs per ton of the gross weight.

Conditions under which the formula applies.
1. The permanent way in good order.
2. The engine, tender, and train in good order. The train consisting of six-wheeled carriages lubricated with grease.
3. A straight line of rails.
4. Fair weather, and dry and clean rails.
5. An average side-wind, of average strength, varying (in the experiments) from *slight* to VERY STRONG.

The resistance may be considerably augmented by unfavourable circumstances. By a combination of frequent curves under one mile

---

18. See '*Railway Machinery*', page 264.

radius, with strong side and headwinds, the resistance to traction may be raised 50 per cent. But the above formula is commonly employed by engineers in calculations for estimating the resistance of trains and the power of locomotives. The annexed table gives the resistance per ton of engine, tender, and train, for various speeds and various gradients, extracted from 'Railway Machinery', page 276:

Ascending Gradients	Conditions A good, sound road. A straight road. An average side-wind. Engine, tender, and train in good working order.						
	Speed in Miles per Hour						
	10	20	30	40	50	60	70
	Total Resistance in lbs per ton. Constant 8lbs						
	lbs	lbs	lbs	lbs	lbs	lbs	lbs
Level	8.6	10.3	13.2	17.3	22.6	29	36.6
1 in 40	64	66	69	73	79	85	93
1 in 60	46	48	50	55	60	66	74
1 in 80	36	38	41	45	51	57	65
1 in 100	31	33	36	40	45	51	59
1 in 150	24	26	28	32	38	44	51
1 in 200	20	22	25	29	34	40	48
1 in 250	18	20	22	26	32	38	46
1 in 300	16	18	21	25	30	36	44
1 in 500	13	15	18	22	27	33	41
1 in 800	11	13	16	20	25	32	39
1 in 1000	11	12	15	19	25	30	39
Level	8.6	10.3	13.2	17.3	22.6	29	36.6

It is worthy of special observation that the resistance of trains – adopting as a standard for comparison the current practice of trains in England – may be considerably modified by the way in which the train is placed on its wheels: for instance, by placing the train on bogie-frames and wheels, and by using oil for the lubrication of the train instead of grease. The results of observations made by the writer, in 1850, on the resistance of waggons, show an extraordinary diversity of resistance, varying from 7½lbs per ton of the train alone, and 13lbs, including the engine, to 29lbs per ton of engine, tender, and train, at speeds under 30 miles per hour. Such extreme diversity is no doubt due to the comparative freedom and state of repair of the waggons and of the way, the state of lubrication, and the curves on the line.

Again, in the working of two coal trains consisting of waggons having inside bearings, the following diversity was exhibited in the gross resistance of engine, tender, and train:

1. At 11 miles per hour, 27lbs per ton.
2. At 13 miles per hour, 18lbs per ton.

The second train had only two-thirds of the resistance of the first, and the advantage was no doubt due chiefly to the lateral play of the journals in the bearings, in the second case; by which the wheels were free to adapt themselves without effort to the rails, swaying towards each side as they might happen to be biassed by conical tyres and uneven rails. In the first case, the want of such play prevented the wheels from so adjusting themselves laterally without at the same time swaying the superincumbent loads. For the low speeds at which the trains were run, the lateral play at the bearings was undoubtedly beneficial.

But the great practical improvement of the day, at least so far as English rolling-stock is concerned, is the substitution of radial axles and axle-boxes, or of bogie-frame and wheels, for the rigid wheel-bases of carriage and waggon-stock: – bogie-frames, that is to say, in so far that individual waggons should be manipulated in the train as bogies, if not even to the extent of placing waggons of a larger class on a pair of bogies; and rigid wheel-bases, that is to say, in so far that in common practice the axles of a carriage or a waggon are put in and maintained in positions parallel to each other, without the option of swivelling to curves. The practice in the United States of the universal adoption of bogies under the engines, tenders, carriages, and waggons, is well worthy of analysis; and, whilst it is maintained, with truth, that the bogie is essential on the imperfect roads of America to enable the wheels to follow the rails, and thus to obviate the chances of derailment, it must also be affirmed that, by means of the bogie, the tractive resistance of engines and trains is notably less than that of a parallel-axled stock.

In connection with the bogie, or the radial-axle, the general use of oil for lubricating axles further reduces the resistance to traction as compared with the use of grease. These are, therefore, in the immediate future, the things to be done: the general adoption of the radiating system in rolling-stock, and the general substitution of oil for grease in lubrication.

In the application of the bogie-principle to waggons, it may not, in many cases, be advisable to place two distinct bogies, with eight wheels, under one waggon, but at least an equivalent adaptation may be effected by applying the tractive force to a central point in the waggon; it may even be a solid central pivot from which point the waggon is to be drawn, and by which point it is to be connected to the following waggon. Were such a system of traction generally employed in place of the common system by which, a fixed overhanging draw-hook at each end of the waggon is seized, the necessary tractive force would be very materially reduced on straight lines as well as on curves; for whilst the waggon would continue to be the medium for the transmission of tractive force, it would be left at full liberty to play over the rails and to suit itself to irregularities, thus obviating a quantity of sledging action which arises from the unavoidable binding of rolling stock on the rails when coupled in the usual manner, by substituting a movement more nearly akin to simple rolling. But in whatever form the radial principle, or the principle of the bogie, is to be worked out in English rolling-stock, the fact is certain that the resistance to traction will be reduced and the durability of the stock augmented. Mr Zerah Colburn describes very specifically a course of experiments which he conducted with a goods engine and train, wheeled on the bogie system, on the New York and Erie Railroad, over a total distance of 900 miles, on various gradients. The engine had four coupled wheels and a bogie, the total weight in working order being 29½ tons, of which 17⅞ tons rested on the coupled wheels available for adhesion. The coupled wheels were 5 feet in diameter. The cylinders, which were outside, were 17 inches in diameter, and the stroke 24 inches. The safety-valves were set to blow-off at 130lbs per square inch; and the steam, as observed by a Bourdon gauge, was seldom allowed to exceed that limit. The tender, loaded, weighed 18½ tons. The train consisted of eight-wheeled waggons, fully loaded with deals, the average weight of each waggon, empty, being 5 tons 8 cwts 3 qrs; and that of each waggon, with its load, 15 tons 5 cwts 3 qrs, nearly. The waggons had cast-iron chilled wheels, 30 inches in diameter, with inside journals 3⅞ inches in diameter and 8 inches long. All the waggons had been put in complete order, and the journals, fitted with oil-tight boxes, were kept well oiled. The line had a gauge of 6 feet. The weather was most favourable – clear and dry – for the whole time of the trial, with the exception of a single day of heavy rain.

Upon about 100 miles of the line, forming a portion of the Susquehanna division, a train of 100 waggons, weighing, with engine and tender, 1,572 tons, was taken. The train was a few feet more than half a mile in length.

At one point it was stopped, when the line commenced an ascent of 24 feet in 4 miles, average 1 in 800 for the whole distance. There were also long and easy curves on this portion. The train was taken up and purposely stopped on the second mile, to be sure of starting again with no aid from momentum. The average speed up was 5 miles per hour; and neither was the pressure of steam increased nor sand used, except in starting from the stops purposely made. The engine, even were its full boiler-pressure of 130lbs maintained as effective pressure upon the piston throughout the whole length of their stock, could not have exerted a tractive force greater than –

$$\frac{172 \times 130\text{lbs} \times 2 \text{ feet}}{5 \text{ feet}} = 15,028\text{lbs}$$

nor is it at all probable that the effective cylinder-pressure could have approached this limit by from 10lbs to 15lbs per square inch. Supposing, however, for the sake of a *reductio ad absurdum,* that the full boiler-pressure had been maintained upon the pistons for the whole length of their strokes, the adhesion of the coupled driving-wheels, not deducting the internal resistance of the engines, would have been $(^1/_4 \, ^5/_0 \, ^0/_0 \, ^2/_5 \, ^8/_0 =)$ $^3/_8$ths of the weight upon them. In any case, there was a resistance of 4,011lbs due to gravity; and if even 120lbs effective cylinder-pressure be assumed, corresponding to a total tractive force of 13,872lbs, the quotient representing the rolling and other resistances, exclusive of gravity, would be but 6.27lbs per ton of the entire train – a resistance including all the internal resistances of the engine, the resistance of the curves, easy as they were, and the loss in accelerating and retarding the trains in starting and stopping. This estimate of resistance would correspond, at the observed speed of 5 miles per hour (upwards of three-quarters of an hour having been consumed in the 4 miles), to 185 indicator horsepower, which with the driving-wheels making but 28 revolutions per minute, would be the utmost that an engine with but 1,031 square feet of heating surface could be expected to exert. This was the highest result observed during the three weeks, but one or two others are worthy of mention. On the Delaware division of the same line, the train of 1,572 tons weight was run over five consecutive miles of absolutely level line at a mean rate of 9.23 miles an hour, and during the same day over five other consecutive miles of level, at a mean rate of 9.70 miles per hour. On both levels there were 14½-chain curves of good length; and the speed – from 9 to 12 miles per hour – at which the train entered the respective levels was not quite regularly maintained through the half hour expended in running over them. But if even 7lbs per ton of the total weight be taken as the resistance at these speeds, the tractive force will be 11,004lbs, which is more than one-fourth of the adhesion-weight of 40,050lbs. On the next day, the same engine hauled 30 waggons, weighing 466½ tons, or, including engine and tender, 514 tons, nearly, up a gradient of 1 in 117½, three miles long, at a mean speed of 10¼ miles an hour. The resistance due to gravity was 9,814lbs; and, supposing the other resistances to traction to amount to no more than 7lbs per ton, the total resistance would be 13,412lbs, corresponding to a mean effective cylinder-pressure of 117lbs per square inch, and to a coefficient of adhesion of almost exactly one-third."[19]

There is nothing very improbable in these results of the performance of the engine, when it is considered that every waggon was placed on double bogies, though it must be confessed, with Mr Colburn, that the result is in some respects unique in the history of railway traction. He has estimated, from his experiments, that the gross resistance of the engine, tender, and train could not have been more than from 6¼lbs to 7lbs per ton at a speed of from 5 to 10 miles per hour. In comparison with this rate of resistance, the gross resistance of the Great Western engine and train, at 10 miles per hour, was 8½lbs per ton on a straight line, with average side-winds.

Corroborative of the results of Mr Colburn, Mr E. A. Cowper brought forward the results of experiments he made to test, by means of a dynamometer, the tractive resistance of ordinary carriages of the London and South-Western Railway, fitted with Mr Joseph Beattie's closed oil axle-boxes; in some cases one carriage only, and in others two carriages, being towed. The force required to start the carriage amounted in some cases to 4lbs per ton, and in others the friction was only 2.1lbs per ton to keep the carriage just in motion when the rails were level. In another case, a force of 2lbs per ton of the gross load was sufficient to keep the carriage just in motion on level rails. At a speed of 15 miles per hour the friction was 2.4lbs per ton, and at 25 miles per hour it was 2.8lbs per ton. Similarly, the friction of waggons weighing from 6 to 7 tons, with white metal bearings and close oil-boxes, averaged 2.85lbs per ton.[20]

The effect of the foregoing evidence is, that a constant resistance of 8lbs per ton, which has been usually adopted in calculations of the resistance of trains running in grease, is likely to be succeeded ultimately by a constant resistance of 4lbs or 5lbs per ton with oil-lubrication. But the great source of economy lies in the substitution of the principle of the bogie for the sledge-like action of fixed parallel axles; for, by this means, not only the constant element of resistance, but likewise the variable resistance, will be materially diminished, and will bring with it a material reduction in the cost of maintenance as well as of engine-power. All experience

---

19. See a paper by Mr Zerah Colburn, on 'American Locomotives and Boiling Stock', in the *Proceedings of the Institution of Civil Engineers*, 1868–69, vol. xxviii., page 370.
20. The same Volume, page 406.

shows that the grinding of wheels fixed on parallel axles, especially the leading-wheels of engines in passing along quick curves, absorbs a good deal of power: that must be the case wherever there is a long wheel-base with parallel axles. The writer found that with a passenger-train on the Caledonian Railway, going at the rate of 45 miles per hour, the resistance was increased from 28lbs to 34lbs per ton gross, or 21½ per cent., as measured by the indicator on the cylinder, when the train passed from a portion of the line which was practically straight, to a portion of the line having curves of less than 1 mile radius, but more than half a mile radius, averaging $2^5/8$ curves per mile. The great extra resistance must have been caused by – more than anything else – the obliquity of the axles, or their want of squareness with the rails; and it is evident that where, by the use of the bogie-system, the axles are brought into the desired state of squareness with the rails – particularly the leading axle of the engine – the resistance on curves must be comparatively approximated to that on straight lines. Any one who has observed a heavy-laden waggon turning a street corner, grinding on the kerbstone, must have been struck with the great strain in pushing the wheels sidewise; and it is precisely this lateral straining, or surging, involving extra resistance, that takes place every time an engine with parallel axles passes along a curve. End play in the axle-boxes, it is true, prevents binding in curves; but this can be better prevented by widening the gauge, though the prevention of binding does not mitigate the chief objection to parallel axles. The writer has observed that, for engines in passing along the quick curves of sidings, the indicator-resistance has been more than twice as much as that upon a straight line.

Chapter 26

Resistance for Steep Inclines

A good means for judging of the resistance of different forms of engines is to compare their performance on steep inclines, with which quick curves are usually associated. For this purpose the results of the performance of a number of engines on inclines are given in the table on page 174,[21] abstracted partly from published statements, and partly from the observations of the writer. The performances are reduced, for the sake of a direct comparison, to equivalent performances as on the steepest incline on the list – namely, 1 in 27, on the Mauritius Railway. It appears that the Semmering engines, having coupled parallel axles, take three times their adhesion-weight. The Giovi engines, being two tank-engines coupled together, take an equivalent little more than two and a half times their adhesion-weight. The Mauritius engines, having coupled parallel axles, take three times their adhesion-weight. The coupled engines on the Santander Railway, with a bogie in front, take an equivalent four times their adhesion-weight. The four-coupled-wheel tank-engines on the Great North of Scotland Railway take up five times their adhesion-weight; and the four-coupled goods-engines, with a bogie in front, on the same line, take up six times their adhesion-weight. The amounts given are averages. They clearly show that the bogie-engine is more efficient than the ordinary multi-coupled engine without bogies. The comparatively small performance of the Giovi engines is a consequence of the ordinary but defective mode of coupling the engines together, namely, a short central coupling with a great overhang from the wheel-base, which induces a great leverage to bind the engines hard against the inner rail on curves. The advantage of the bogie is very directly shown in comparing the two engines on the Great North of Scotland line. The four-coupled-wheel tank-engines weigh 25 tons, all adhesion-weight; and they move an equivalent gross load, including their own weight, of 130 tons. The bogie-engine, with only 17½ tons adhesion-weight, moves an equivalent gross load of 110 tons; that is, with about two-thirds adhesion-weight, they take six-sevenths of the gross load taken by the tank-engines.

---

21. This table is copied from an article written by the author, on Resistance of Trains, in 'Locomotive Engineering', page 293.

Name or Locality	Adhesive Weight	Weight of Engine and Tender	Weight of Train	Gross Weight of Engine, Tender, and Train	Ascending Gradient
	Tons	Tons	Tons	Tons	
1. Semmering Incline	37.5	59	130	189	1 in 40
2. Semmering Incline	46.5	66	175	241	1 in 40
3. Semmering Incline	37	56.4	100	156.4	1 in 40
4. Great North of Scotland, bogie and tender	17.5	43	189	232	1 in 75
5. Great North of Scotland, bogie and tender	17.5	43	144	187	1 in 50
6. Great North of Scotland, tank-engine	25	25	209	234	1 in 59
7. Great North of Scotland, tank-engine	25	25	231	256	1 in 59
8. Giovi incline, two tank-engines coupled together	55	55	100	155	1 in 29
9. Mauritius Railway	48	48	100	148	1 in 27
10. Santander Railway	36	45	200	245	1 in 50

No. Gross Weights or Loads reduced for a Gradient of 1 in 27.

1.	135 tons gross =		3.6 times 37.5 tons adhesive weight
2.	173 tons gross =	3.4	3.72 times 46.4 tons adhesive weight
3.	112 tons gross =		3.02 times 37 tons adhesive weight
4.	103 tons gross	6¼	6.0 times 17.5 tons adhesive weight
5.	112 tons gross		6.4 times 17.5 tons adhesive weight
6.	123 tons gross	5¼	5.0 times 25 tons adhesive weight
7.	135 tons gross =		5.4 times 25 tons adhesive weight
8.	145 tons gross =		2.6 times 55 tons adhesive weight
9.	148 tons gross =		3.0 times 48 tons adhesive weight
10.	147 tons gross =		4.0 times 36 tons adhesive weight

Index